OREGON ROCKS!

A Guide to 60 Amazing Geologic Sites

MARLI B. MILLER

PHOTOGRAPHS BY THE AUTHOR

2021
Mountain Press Publishing Company
Missoula, Montana

GEOLOGY ROCKS!

A state-by-state series that introduces readers to some of the most compelling and accessible geologic sites in each state.

Text and photographs © 2021 Marli Miller
First Printing, April 2021
Second Printing, February 2022

Maps and figures constructed by Chelsea M. Feeney
(www.cmcfeeney.com)

COVER PHOTO: View southward from the top of Spencer Butte.

Library of Congress Cataloging-in-Publication Data

Names: Miller, Marli Bryant, 1960- author.
Title: Oregon rocks! : a guide to 60 amazing geologic sites / Marli B. Miller.
Description: First. | Missoula, Montana : Mountain Press Publishing Company, 2021. | Series: Geology rocks! | Includes bibliographical references and index. | Summary: "To discover astonishing rocks and landforms in Oregon, all that is required is a good map, a sense of adventure, and *Oregon Rocks*, a guide to 60 of the most compelling geologic sites in the state." —Provided by publisher.
Identifiers: LCCN 2021003028 | ISBN 9780878427031 (paperback)
Subjects: LCSH: Geology—Oregon—Guidebooks. | Oregon—Guidebooks.
Classification: LCC QE155 .M55 2021 | DDC 557.95—dc23
LC record available at https://lccn.loc.gov/2021003028

PRINTED IN THE UNITED STATES BY VERSA PRESS

Mountain Press
PUBLISHING COMPANY
P.O. Box 2399 • Missoula, MT 59806 • 406-728-1900
800-234-5308 • info@mtnpress.com
www.mountain-press.com

PREFACE AND ACKNOWLEDGMENTS

In 2014, I remember feeling a combination of joy and sadness while finishing up *Roadside Geology of Oregon*: joy because I was finally completing such a large project, and sadness because I thought I was finished writing about Oregon's geology. Writing *Oregon Rocks!* pushed me to discover Oregon all over again—and to visit some new places entirely. I have so enjoyed these past three years and I've learned so much!

The sixty sites described in this book are fascinating places, from calderas to coastal headlands to deep desert canyons to alpine peaks. While each makes a great destination for a geology field trip, most sites also offer multiple opportunities for explorations and personal discoveries that go well beyond this book. And together, they tell Oregon's geologic history. Beginning with the formation and accretion of the disparate crustal fragments that geologists call terranes, this history continues with recent volcanic activity and earthquakes, and the ever-present erosion that continually shapes our landscape.

Sites that lie close to each other on the landscape don't necessarily tell geologic stories that lie close to each other in geologic time. In the Wallowa Mountains, for example, site 52 (Wallowa Lake) illustrates glacial moraines that were deposited 25,000 to 17,000 years ago, whereas site 53 (waterfall above Hurricane Creek) highlights rocks of an accreted terrane that formed more than 200 million years ago. To help place the sites within the context of Oregon's geologic history, I included site numbers on the timeline of page vi as well as the cross section and location map on page 4.

At the bottom of the first page of each site, I listed the primary references I used to help educate myself about a given place. The geologic maps produced by the Oregon Department of Geology and Mineral Industries (DOGAMI) and the US Geological Survey (USGS) proved especially useful and are generally available online. Of course, I learned the most from my own visits to these wonderful places, and I made a point to describe the features I could actually see.

Unquestionably, my greatest joy in this book project derived from the many people who helped. First and foremost, Kevin Shanley encouraged and inspired me—and accompanied me to dozens of the sites. My editor, Jenn Carey, answered my endless questions and arranged my oversupply of photographs and long descriptions into something I'm really proud of. I'm grateful for our wonderful working relationship that has grown since we first worked together more than ten years ago. Chelsea Feeney greatly improved on my original versions of the maps and diagrams. Jeannie Painter created the beautiful layout.

I thank the many friends and colleagues who made suggestions, provided materials, and even reviewed sections of the manuscript. I would especially like to thank Marisa Acosta, Ellen Bishop, Sammy Castonguay (who also took me into the field), Jad D'Allura, Natalia Deligne, Ted Fremd, Thomas Giacchetti, Samantha Hopkins, Daniele Mckay, Josh Roering, John Roth, and Ray Weldon.

And finally, thanks to friends and colleagues for putting me up at their places while I did my field work. Ilya Bindeman; Ellen Bishop; Sammy, Laurie, Oshen, Neva, and Manny Castonguay; Alyse and Joe Gass; Maria Gibson and Shane Daugherty; Doug Norseth and Bruce Hegna; John Stockham and Carol Schunk—you made this project so much more fun than I thought possible!

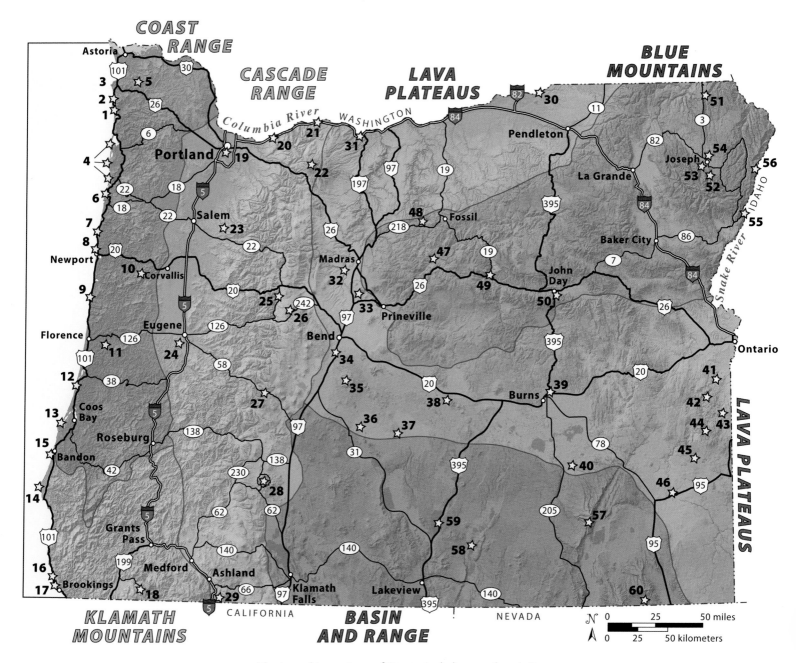

Physiographic provinces of Oregon including numbered sites.

CONTENTS

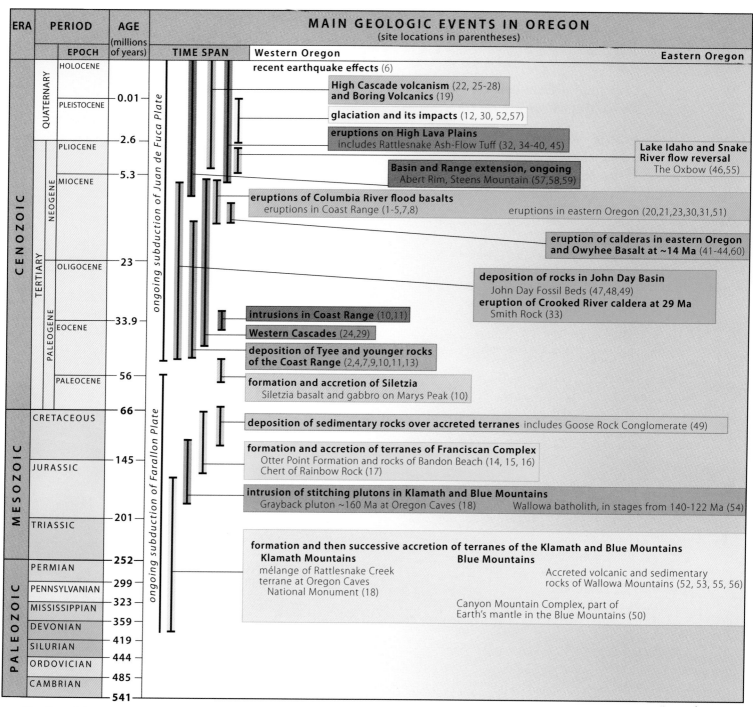

ERA	PERIOD		AGE (millions of years)	TIME SPAN	MAIN GEOLOGIC EVENTS IN OREGON (site locations in parentheses)	
		EPOCH			Western Oregon	Eastern Oregon

MAIN GEOLOGIC EVENTS IN OREGON
(site locations in parentheses)

recent earthquake effects (6)

High Cascade volcanism (22, 25-28) and Boring Volcanics (19)

glaciation and its impacts (12, 30, 52,57)

eruptions on High Lava Plains includes Rattlesnake Ash-Flow Tuff (32, 34-40, 45)

Lake Idaho and Snake River flow reversal The Oxbow (46,55)

Basin and Range extension, ongoing Abert Rim, Steens Mountain (57,58,59)

eruptions of Columbia River flood basalts eruptions in Coast Range (1-5,7,8)   eruptions in eastern Oregon (20,21,23,30,31,51)

eruption of calderas in eastern Oregon and Owyhee Basalt at ~14 Ma (41-44,60)

deposition of rocks in John Day Basin John Day Fossil Beds (47,48,49)
eruption of Crooked River caldera at 29 Ma Smith Rock (33)

intrusions in Coast Range (10,11)

Western Cascades (24,29)

deposition of Tyee and younger rocks of the Coast Range (2,4,7,9,10,11,13)

formation and accretion of Siletzia Siletzia basalt and gabbro on Marys Peak (10)

deposition of sedimentary rocks over accreted terranes includes Goose Rock Conglomerate (49)

formation and accretion of terranes of Franciscan Complex Otter Point Formation and rocks of Bandon Beach (14, 15, 16) Chert of Rainbow Rock (17)

intrusion of stitching plutons in Klamath and Blue Mountains Grayback pluton ~160 Ma at Oregon Caves (18)   Wallowa batholith, in stages from 140-122 Ma (54)

formation and then successive accretion of terranes of the Klamath and Blue Mountains
Klamath Mountains   Blue Mountains
mélange of Rattlesnake Creek terrane at Oregon Caves National Monument (18)   Accreted volcanic and sedimentary rocks of Wallowa Mountains (52, 53, 55, 56)
Canyon Mountain Complex, part of Earth's mantle in the Blue Mountains (50)

ongoing subduction of Juan de Fuca Plate

ongoing subduction of Farallon Plate

Timeline of the main geologic events in Oregon. Events are placed on the chart relative to their position in Oregon, with events that affected western Oregon on the left and those that affected eastern Oregon on the right. Numbers in parentheses refer to localities described in this book. Ages in millions of years (Ma). The same sequence of events can be inferred from the cross section on page 4.

A BRIEF GEOLOGIC HISTORY OF OREGON

Oregon's landscape ranges from coastal headlands to mountains to colorful canyons and tells a multitude of geological stories. The rock, forming the landscape's underlying foundation, speaks to ancient environments and events, while the shape of the land tells how it's been fashioned by erosion. From Crater Lake to John Day Fossil Beds, this book highlights the geology of sixty of Oregon's most dramatic landscapes. The sites are organized into six chapters, each covering one of Oregon's six physiographic regions. The Coast Range and Klamath Mountains occupy the coastal part of the state, the Cascade Range forms a north-south mountainous spine, and the Blue Mountains, Lava Plateaus, and Basin and Range make up the comparatively arid, eastern side of the state.

From its oldest rocks to its youngest, Oregon has been profoundly affected by plate tectonics, the process by which Earth's outer shell, or lithosphere, is broken into gigantic fragments, called plates. They slowly drift on the order of a few centimeters per year over an underlying zone called the asthenosphere, and as they do, they interact with each other along their margins. These interactions form mountain belts, trigger earthquakes, and provide magma for volcanoes. Plate motions have particularly influenced Oregon, with its position near the western edge of the North American Plate.

Some 300 miles off the Oregon coast, the East Pacific Rise marks a divergent plate boundary where the Pacific and Juan de Fuca Plates are moving away from each other. As they pull apart, volcanic material erupts along the axis, called a spreading ridge, to create new oceanic lithosphere. The spreading ridge consists of a series of noncontinuous segments linked by transform faults, places where plates move side-by-side with respect to each other.

As the Juan de Fuca Plate moves northeastward away from the spreading center, it converges with the North American Plate at the Cascadia subduction zone. The Juan de Fuca

Plate is the denser of the two plates, so it subducts (sinks) beneath the less dense North American Plate. As it subducts, it heats up and causes dehydration of water-rich minerals in the plate. The water rises into the overlying North American

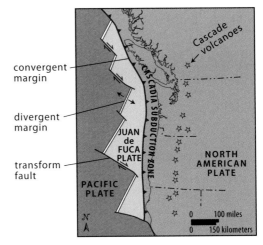

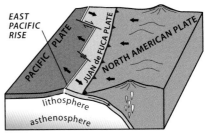

Map and block diagram illustrating the plate tectonic setting of the Pacific Northwest. As the Juan de Fuca Plate (in blue) subducts beneath North America, it causes melting, which generates the magma for the volcanic activity in the Cascades. —From Miller, 2014

1

Plate to cause melting. As the continental rocks melt, the resulting magma fuels today's Cascade volcanoes.

Evidence of volcanic chains in Oregon that pre-date today's High Cascades speak to subduction that extends back in time. Many of Oregon's granitic bodies, such as the Wallowa batholith in the northeast corner of the state or Grayback pluton in the Klamaths, originally formed as magma chambers above a subduction zone, as long as 160 million years ago. Volcanic rocks of the Clarno Formation and similar rocks exposed throughout much of central Oregon formed from about 49 to 40 million years ago. The Western Cascades, now deeply eroded, began erupting 40 to 35 million years ago and continued until about 5 million years ago.

Plate motions, especially subduction, also cause the addition, or accretion, of material to the edges of continents. Imagine a topographically high area, such as an oceanic plateau or series of oceanic islands, on a subducting oceanic plate: when it encounters the subduction zone, it will resist the process, sometimes even causing subduction to stop. Eventually, a new subduction zone may break farther offshore, adding the high area to the edge of the plate. These accreted bodies of rock, called terranes, form the underlying basement of the entire state of Oregon.

WEST   EAST

approximate sea level

NORTH AMERICA

oceanic lithosphere   continental lithosphere

A. The oceanic plate approaching North America contains rock and sediment of a seamount. The package of rock may be several different terranes faulted together.

B. The rock and sediment collide with North America.

C. The package of rock has been accreted, and a new subduction zone forms to the west.

Schematic view of the process of continental accretion during subduction.
—From Miller, 2014

Volcanic Activity in Oregon

Without a doubt, Oregon has more recently active volcanoes as well as a more volcanic geologic history than any other state in the conterminous United States. In fact, many of its sedimentary rocks contain volcanic particles, and many metamorphic rocks formed from preexisting volcanic rocks. Oregon's Cascade Range, actively fueled by ongoing subduction to the west, contains all types of volcanoes: cinder cones, shield volcanoes, stratovolcanoes, domes, and calderas. Altogether, the US Geological Survey estimates the range to have more than one thousand Quaternary-age volcanic vents. Numerous volcanoes spread out east of the Cascades as well.

The shape of a volcano, as well as its explosivity, is related to the chemical composition of its lava. In general, the lower the silica content, the more fluid the lava and the more likely it will flow a great distance from the vent. Consequently, basaltic eruptions, which are low in silica, result in shield volcanoes that have a relatively subdued profile. Moreover, because of their fluidity, the lavas don't build up great pressures at the vent and so result in comparatively mild eruptions. Relatively small explosive eruptions can form when there is abundant water or gas, and in these cases a vent may create a cinder cone.

In contrast, andesitic volcanoes, which carry more silica in their lavas, are less fluid and build steeper slopes to form high stratovolcanoes, such as Mt. Hood (site 22) and Mt. Jefferson. Their lavas also build up high pressures at the vents, and the eruptions tend to be much more explosive. Much

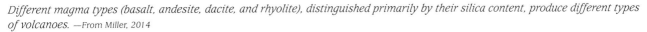

decreases ← *silica content* → **increases**

basalt

andesite

dacite-rhyolite

  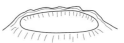 

Shield Volcano
Low gradient and large. Consists of basaltic lava flows that were relatively fluid; may have cinder cones on flanks.
(examples:
  Newberry Volcano, McKenzie Pass, Diamond Craters)

Cinder Cone
Steep, relatively small conical hills that consist of cinders erupted from a central vent.
(examples:
  Lava Butte, Jordan Craters)

Stratovolcano Composite Volcano
Steep and large. Consists mostly of andesitic and pyroclastic material (explosive products like ash and pumice); may consist of two or more coalesced volcanoes.
(examples:
  Mt. Hood, McKenzie Pass)

Caldera
Steep-sided depression, typically 100s to 1000s of feet deep and more than a mile across; formed by collapse of volcano into emptied magma chamber after major eruption.
(examples:
  Crater Lake, Smith Rock, McDermitt caldera)

Dome volcano
Very steep gradient but relatively small features, made out of dacitic or rhyolitic lava, which tends to be very viscous (sticky) and so cannot travel far from the vent.
(examples:
  domes at Crater Lake, Glass Buttes)

Different magma types (basalt, andesite, dacite, and rhyolite), distinguished primarily by their silica content, produce different types of volcanoes. —From Miller, 2014

of the Oregon Cascades consist of basaltic andesite, which forms lava flows very much like basalt, but intermediate in chemistry between basalt and andesite.

The lavas with the most silica, dacite and rhyolite, tend to be so viscous that they don't flow very far or they plug up the vent to form domes. In the case of sufficient water or gas, they erupt catastrophically to form calderas. Big Obsidian Flow at Newberry (site 35) is rhyolite, whereas the eruption of Mt. Mazama some 7,700 years ago to form the Crater Lake caldera was a dacite eruption (site 28).

PALEOZOIC THROUGH MESOZOIC ERAS

Oregon's geologic history dates back to the Devonian Period of the Paleozoic Era but is difficult to describe in concrete terms because most of the rocks from that early time didn't form in Oregon, let alone in North America. Instead, they formed offshore as pieces of oceanic lithosphere, fragments of island arcs, deep ocean basins, or even as subduction zones. They were accreted to the edge of North America at various times between about 150 and 100 million years ago. You can see some of these rocks up

close at Oregon Caves National Monument (site 18) in the Klamath Mountains, or in several different sites in the Blue Mountains, including the Wallowa Mountains (sites 53, 54) and Hells Canyon (sites 55, 56).

The multiple accretionary events accompanied melting in the lower crust, and the resulting granitic magmas intruded the terranes, locally cutting across terrane boundaries. Called stitching plutons because they appear to stitch the terranes together, their ages range from about 160 to 120 million years and help establish when the various terranes came together. In addition, the hot fluids from these crystallizing magmas provided the ultimate sources of many of Oregon's precious metals. In the Klamath Mountains, dikes from the Grayback pluton intrude accreted marble at Oregon Caves National Monument (site 18). In the Blue Mountains, granitic rock of the Wallowa batholith intrudes the accreted Wallowa terrane and forms much of the spectacular landscape near the town of Joseph (site 54).

The Franciscan Complex, present along southwestern Oregon's coastline and extending southward into California, formed and welded to North America after the accretion of the Blue Mountains and Klamath terranes. It originated as a collection of widely different rock types that came together in a subduction zone between about 150 and 65 million

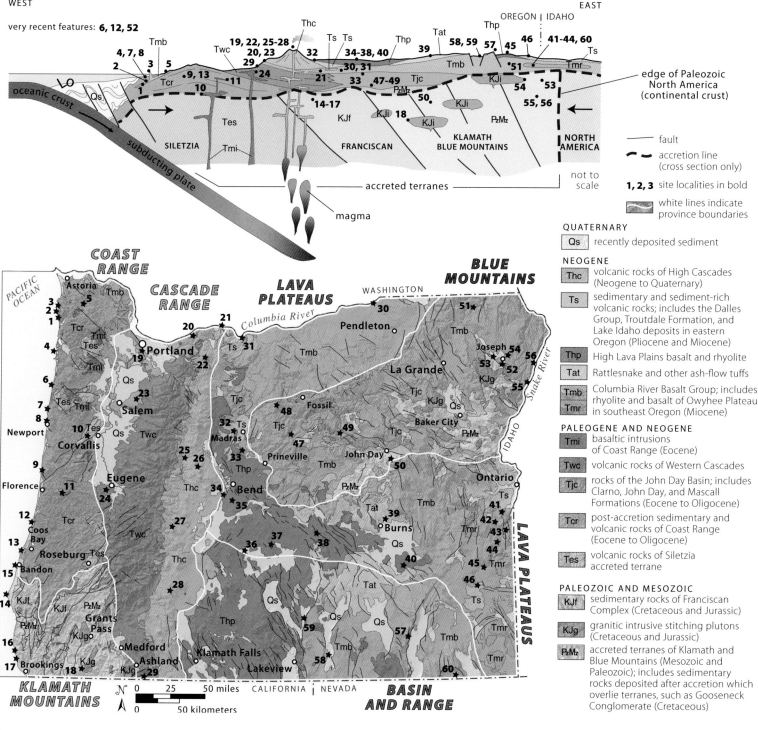

WEST

very recent features: **6, 12, 52**

OREGON | IDAHO

EAST

19, 22, 25-28
20, 23
4, 7, 8
Tmb
Twc
29
32
Ts Ts
34-38, 40
Thp
Tat
58, 59
57
Thp
45
46
41-44, 60
Thc
39
2
3
5
30, 31
Tmb
51
Ts
1
Tcr
9, 13
24
21
33
47-49
Tjc
KJi
54
53
oceanic crust
Qs
10
14-17
33
47-49
50
KJi
55, 56
LO

Tes
KJf
KJi
18
KJi
PzMz

subducting plate
Tmi
SILETZIA
FRANCISCAN
KLAMATH
BLUE MOUNTAINS
NORTH
AMERICA

accreted terranes

magma

edge of Paleozoic
North America
(continental crust)

—— fault

▬▬ accretion line
(cross section only)

not to
scale

1, 2, 3 site localities in bold

white lines indicate
province boundaries

COAST RANGE
PACIFIC OCEAN
Astoria
Tmb
CASCADE RANGE
LAVA PLATEAUS
WASHINGTON
Columbia River
BLUE MOUNTAINS
3
2
5
Tcr
Tmi
Tes
21
20
Ts
31
30
51
Tmb
1
Joseph
54
56
4
Tmi
19
Portland
22
Pendleton
53
52
KJg
55
Snake River
6
Tes
Tmi
23
Salem
La Grande
7
Qs
Tjc
KJg
Qs
8
Newport
10
Tes
Corvallis
Qs
Twc
32
Madras
Ts
48
Fossil
Tjc
Baker City
PzMz
Ontario
Ts
9
33
Tjc
49
IDAHO
41
Florence
Thp
25
26
Prineville
John Day
42
11
24
Thc
34
Bend
Tmb
50
43
12
Tcr
27
35
PzMz
Tat
39
44
Coos Bay
Twc
36
37
38
Burns
45
Tmr
13
Roseburg
Tes
Thc
Qs
40
46
Ts
15
Bandon
28
Tat
Qs
LAVA PLATEAUS
14
KJf
PzMz
Qs
Qs
57
Tmr
KJf
Grants Pass
Thp
59
Tmb
KJg
PzMz
Medford
Klamath Falls
58
16
KJg
Ashland
Lakeview
Tmr
17
Brookings
18
KJg
29
60
KLAMATH MOUNTAINS
CALIFORNIA | NEVADA
BASIN AND RANGE

N
0   25   50 miles
0   50 kilometers

QUATERNARY

Qs recently deposited sediment

NEOGENE

Thc volcanic rocks of High Cascades
(Neogene to Quaternary)

Ts sedimentary and sediment-rich
volcanic rocks; includes the Dalles
Group, Troutdale Formation, and
Lake Idaho deposits in eastern
Oregon (Pliocene and Miocene)

Thp High Lava Plains basalt and rhyolite

Tat Rattlesnake and other ash-flow tuffs

Tmb Columbia River Basalt Group; includes
Tmr rhyolite and basalt of Owyhee Plateau
in southeast Oregon (Miocene)

PALEOGENE AND NEOGENE

Tmi basaltic intrusions
of Coast Range (Eocene)

Twc volcanic rocks of Western Cascades

Tjc rocks of the John Day Basin; includes
Clarno, John Day, and Mascall
Formations (Eocene to Oligocene)

Tcr post-accretion sedimentary and
volcanic rocks of Coast Range
(Eocene to Oligocene)

Tes volcanic rocks of Siletzia
accreted terrane

PALEOZOIC AND MESOZOIC

KJf sedimentary rocks of Franciscan
Complex (Cretaceous and Jurassic)

KJg granitic intrusive stitching plutons
(Cretaceous and Jurassic)

PzMz accreted terranes of Klamath and
Blue Mountains (Mesozoic and
Paleozoic); includes sedimentary
rocks deposited after accretion which
overlie terranes, such as Gooseneck
Conglomerate (Cretaceous)

years ago. The sea stacks of Bandon Beach (site 15), the headland at Cape Blanco (site 14), Indian Sands (site 16), and Rainbow Rock (site 17) all provide outstanding examples of different parts of the Franciscan Complex.

Some sedimentary rocks of Mesozoic age are native to Oregon, deposited late in the Cretaceous Period over the already accreted terranes. They appear as the blue layer at the bottom of the cover sequence on the cross section. These rocks include both river deposits and shallow to deep-water ocean deposits. One of the better-known rock units, the Goose Rock Conglomerate, forms beautiful outcrops in the Sheep Rock Unit of the John Day Fossil Beds National Monument (site 49).

CENOZOIC ERA

Oregon's early Cenozoic history is represented by Siletzia, North America's youngest accreted terrane. Having formed as a giant oceanic plateau between about 56 and 49 million years ago, it consists almost of entirely of basalt, much of which displays beautiful pillow shapes from erupting underwater. Victor Camp of San Diego State University and Ray Wells of the US Geological Survey described evidence that Siletzia formed as an early expression of the Yellowstone hot spot. Siletzia accreted to North America between about 51 and 49 million years ago and now forms the basement of the Coast Range, extending from near Roseburgn, north to southern Vancouver Island in British Columbia. Marys Peak, the highest mountain in the Coast Range, contains some outstanding examples of Siletzia's pillow basalt (site 10).

All younger rocks in Oregon formed on North America, over the top of the accreted terranes, and so belong to the cover sequence shown in the cross section on the previous page. Given Oregon's large size, different conditions—resulting in the formation of different rock types—frequently prevailed in different places. Soon after the accretion of Siletzia, for example, marine conditions dominated western Oregon. The Tyee Formation, the most widespread rock unit of the Coast Range, was deposited in a submarine fan complex that deepened northward. At the same time, andesitic volcanism formed the Clarno Formation in central Oregon. Younger rocks of the Coast Range include the deltaic Coaledo Formation, the Yachats volcanic rocks, and the Astoria Formation, which was deposited in deep to shallow ocean water in Miocene time.

Beginning about 40 million years ago, as subduction became reestablished after accretion of Siletzia, the volcanoes of the Western Cascades began producing a variety of lavas and pyroclastic deposits similar to today's High Cascades. They also include numerous intrusive bodies, some of which, like Spencer Butte (site 24) near Eugene or Pilot Rock (site 29) near Ashland, reached shallow levels of the crust before cooling and crystallizing. During this time, several large calderas also erupted east of the Cascades. One of these, the 29.5-million-year-old Crooked River caldera, erupted more than 140 cubic miles of material, some of which forms the cliffs of Smith Rock State Park (site 33).

Material from these volcanic sources accumulated farther east as the John Day Formation. Together with the underlying Clarno Formation and overlying Mascall and Rattlesnake Formations, these rocks record long-term climatic cooling from about 40 to 7 million years ago, with a warm spike between about 16 and 14 million years ago. These rocks also host a spectacular array of plant and animal fossils, whose evolution tracks the changing climate.

Oregon's most widespread rock unit, the Columbia River Basalt Group, erupted from 16.8 until about 6 million years ago. Called flood basalts because they literally flooded northern Oregon and southern Washington, the lavas cover an area greater than 77,000 square miles with a volume greater than 50,000 cubic miles. Some of the flows even reached the Pacific Ocean and, in some cases, invaded the

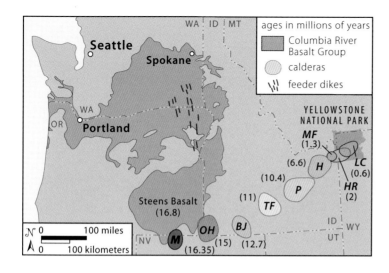

ages in millions of years

Columbia River Basalt Group

calderas

feeder dikes

Seattle
Spokane

WA
OR
Portland

YELLOWSTONE NATIONAL PARK

MF
(1.3)

(6.6)   H   LC
                  (0.6)
(10.4)
            P   HR
(11)   (2)
Steens Basalt   TF
(16.8)

ID WY

OH   BJ
M (15) (12.7)   UT
(16.35)

NV

N 0   100 miles
   0   100 kilometers

Map showing the extent of the Columbia River Basalt Group and calderas and volcanic fields of the Yellowstone hot spot track across southern Idaho. The letter M marks the McDermitt caldera, the first large caldera of the series; other letters include OH, Owyhee-Humboldt; BJ, Bruneau-Jarbidge; TF, Twin Falls; P, Picabo; H, Heise; HR, Huckleberry Ridge Tuff; MF, Mesa Falls Tuff; LC: Lava Creek Tuff. Ages, given in millions of years, show the approximate timing of the onset of major explosive activity in each caldera. —Ages determined from Drew et al., 2013, Henry et al., 2017, and Colón et al., 2018

existing sediments to form intrusive bodies. Approximately 94 percent of the lava erupted by 14.5 million years ago, which means that upward of 46,000 cubic miles of lava erupted within a period of only 2.3 million years! Given the immensity of the eruptions, their chemistry, and their coincidence in timing with several early calderas along the track of the Yellowstone hot spot, geologists generally accept the two phenomena as part of the same process. Awesome places to see these basaltic flows lie in all of Oregon's six physiographic regions except the Klamath Mountains.

Beginning about 10 million years ago, rhyolitic volcanic eruptions rocked the Lava Plateaus near the center of the state, producing a series of rhyolitic centers that become younger in age toward the west. One of these eruptions, centered near Burns, produced the Rattlesnake Ash-Flow Tuff about 7 million years ago to cover more than 10 percent of the state (site 39). Other eruptions in the series include Glass Buttes between 6.5 and 4.9 million years ago (site 38), and the eruption of the Big Obsidian Flow at Newberry only 1,500 years ago (site 35).

At the same time, crustal extension caused large normal faults to break up much of southern Oregon into the Basin and Range Province. This region offers some of Oregon's most dramatic scenery with uplifted mountain ranges rising thousands of feet above down-dropped basins. The region continues to evolve—as demonstrated by the 1993 Klamath

Falls earthquakes near the northwest edge of the province.

The High Cascades, with its myriad volcano types, started forming 8 or 6 million years ago as volcanic centers in the Western Cascades shifted eastward. Few lava flows from the earlier High Cascade eruptions are exposed because they've been buried by younger flows. However, volcanic mudflows, ash, and volcanic-rich sedimentary deposits adjacent to the High Cascades, such as that seen in the Deschutes Formation at Cove Palisades State Park (site 32), retain the record of earlier eruptions. Today's peaks of the High Cascades are all significantly younger. Mt. Hood (site 22), for example, is considered to have a "long" history because it dates back a half million years. Most of the other volcanoes are considerably younger.

The Pleistocene Epoch, which lasted from about 2.5 million years ago to 10,000 years ago, had a huge effect on Oregon's landscape. Also known as the Pleistocene ice age, this time of recurring cold climates affected the high elevations of the Cascade Range and Blue Mountains, where glaciers carved some of the peaks and left behind telltale glacial moraines. Lower elevations were also affected because the increased precipitation during this time filled many of the basins in southern Oregon with lakes. Those lakes today, such as the Alvord Desert (site 57) or Lake Abert (site 59), are now either dry or filled with a tiny fraction of their original water.

Sea levels during the Pleistocene were some 300 to 450 feet lower than they are today, so the shoreline lay tens of miles west of its present location. With few headlands to block it, sand could freely migrate along the coast; when sea levels rose after the glaciers melted, storms carried the sand onto shore to become Oregon's great coastal dunes. The lower sea levels also allowed rivers to deeply erode their channels. When sea level rose, the oceans inundated the river valleys, creating Oregon's large estuaries.

The most dramatic effect of the ice age came from the Cordilleran ice sheet that advanced into northern Washington, Idaho, and Montana and spawned massive floods, most of which came from Glacial Lake Missoula. These floods, some of which exceeded one hundred times the typical discharge of the Mississippi River, tore up the ground to form scablands, scoured the Columbia River Gorge, deposited thick deposits of coarse gravel, and backed up into giant temporary lakes where they encountered constrictions in the channel. These constrictions include Wallula Gap, where the Columbia River enters Oregon from Washington, just upriver from the scablands at Hat Rock (site 30).

In addition to these colossal ice age floods, the daily grind of erosion by water, wind, and gravity has carved the landscape, removing susceptible parts and leaving behind the more resistant remnants to be eroded at a later date. This effect is especially noticeable along the coast, where resistant headlands protrude westward into the ocean and sea stacks mark former positions of the coastline. Pretty much everywhere you look, the shape of the land results from erosion. In Oregon, the two exceptions to this generalization are recent volcanic activity, where new volcanic rock is added, and recent faulting, which may uplift ridges. In both cases, the key factor is the youthfulness of the volcanic activity or faulting; the younger it is, the less time erosion has had to modify it.

The Umpqua River forms one of Oregon's large estuaries. This location, more than 15 miles from the coast, is affected by Pacific tides.

Lava flows of the Imnaha and Grande Ronde Basalts of the Columbia River Basalt Group in eastern Oregon near Hells Canyon.

Aerial view looking southward over fog-enshrouded Cape Meares. The headland, as well as the sea stacks and headland to the south, consist of lava flows of the Grande Ronde Basalt that flowed here from eastern Oregon.

COAST RANGE

Oregon's Coast Range, a hilly, heavily forested region adjacent to the Pacific Ocean, extends from Bandon and Roseburg north to Astoria and Portland. The deeply eroded mountains reach elevations as high as 4,097 feet at Marys Peak near Corvallis. Westward-flowing rivers drain to the sea, with only the Umpqua and Columbia cutting their channels entirely across the range.

Siletzia, Oregon's most recently accreted terrane, forms the basement of the Coast Range. It's a gigantic terrane, extending northward past Washington's Olympic Mountains to southern Vancouver Island. Siletzia formed as an oceanic plateau between 56 and 49 million years ago and was accreted to North America between 51 and 49 million years ago. Its size, geochemistry, and location suggest it may mark an early phase of the Yellowstone hot spot. In Oregon, Siletzia consists almost entirely of basalt with a minor amount of sandstone. Much of the basalt comes in pillow shapes, formed by blobs of lava whose outer margins chilled when they contacted the cold seawater.

The Coast Range includes central and northern Oregon's rugged coastline, which hosts spectacular headlands, lonely beaches, and a suite of coastal sand dunes that stretches nearly 60 miles. As a general rule, most of the headlands consist of rock that is resistant to erosion, like basalt, whereas most beaches and bays are underlain by less-resistant rock like sandstone. The coastline also features beautiful examples of uplifted marine terraces and even ghost forests, where trees were killed by sudden rises in sea level. Recent faulting activity related to the Cascadia subduction zone—no doubt accompanied by jarring earthquakes—are responsible for the uplifted terraces and drowned forests.

Many of northern Oregon's coastal headlands consist of basalt of the Columbia River Basalt Group, which originated in fissure eruptions in northeastern Oregon and southeastern Washington and coursed all the way to the ocean in Miocene time. Some of these flows followed the Columbia River while others seemed to have crossed low areas in the nascent Coast Range. On reaching the Miocene coastline, many of the lavas poured down a submarine canyon in the vicinity of Saddle Mountain. Because of the high pressures obtained from the continually added basalt, they were able to inject into bedding planes and fractures in the existing sediments, now the Astoria Formation, to form lava-fed magma chambers. Some of these magma chambers are preserved as intrusive bodies parallel to the sedimentary layering, a type of intrusion called a sill. At Neahkahnie Mountain, a sill exceeds 1,000 feet in thickness. Other places, such as Hug Point, may be more instructive because the sills and dikes are small enough to see how they are sandwiched between the enclosing sandstone of the Astoria Formation. At Cannon Beach, the lava reerupted as an undersea volcano, which now forms Haystack Rock. Of course, not all the lava formed intrusions. You can see some beautifully preserved surface flows at Yaquina Head, Cape Meares, and Cape Lookout.

This seemingly impossible story was unraveled through careful mapping, observation, and geochemical analyses beginning in the late 1970s. These studies found that the flows, sills, and dikes along the coast are chemically identical to and of the same age as the 17- to 6-million-year-old Grande Ronde, Wanapum, and Saddle Mountains Basalts, three members of the Columbia River Basalt Group. After a series of technical papers in the 1980s, Ray Wells of the US Geological Survey and a host of his colleagues published a comprehensive professional field guide to the basalt in 2009.

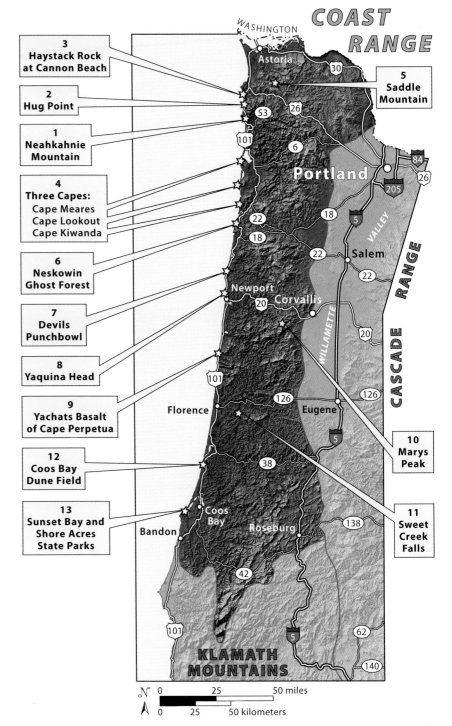

1 NEAHKAHNIE MOUNTAIN
Intrusive Sill of Grande Ronde Basalt

Neahkahnie Mountain, northern Oregon's most imposing feature along US 101, rises more than 1,600 feet above the sea, with sea cliffs giving way to steep forests near the highway level at about 400 feet. No wonder it was the final section of US 101 in Oregon to be built; it opened in 1940. The mountain was revered by the Tillamook-Nehalem peoples and inspired tales of lost treasure among white settlers. Its name stems from a combination of words from the Tillamook and Clatsop languages to approximately mean "Home of the Creator."

From the bottom of its cliffs to its summit, Neahkahnie Mountain consists of more than 1,600 feet of invasive Grande Ronde Basalt. It's a gigantic sill, formed by surface lavas of the Columbia River Basalt Group as they reached the coastline and invaded the local sedimentary sequence.

A close look at the rock shows no air bubbles typical of most surface lava flows because it cooled in the subsurface. Its crystal sizes are intermediate between those of deep igneous intrusions and volcanic rocks because it cooled farther below the surface, and thus more slowly, than a typical lava flow.

Neahkahnie's sea cliffs display a prominent near-vertical set of fractures that guide much of the wave erosion near their base. You can see a small sea cave formed along these fractures by hiking the short trail that leads southwest from the parking lot near the North Trailhead. These fractures likely formed during cooling of the basalt after it invaded the surrounding sedimentary rock. You can also see some of the original, now highly contorted, sedimentary rock by walking to the overlook of Devils Cauldron.

View southward from the viewpoint near milepost 41. US 101 hugs the cliffs of basalt.

 Main sources and further reading: Beeson and others, 1979; Cressy, 1973; Wells and others, 2009

Neahkahnie Mountain as seen looking south from Cape Falcon. Sedimentary rock along the shoreline (left and center) dips toward the intrusive basalt that rises from the shoreline on the far right side of the image to the top of the peak. US 101 passes through the notch above the sea cliffs on the right side of the photo.

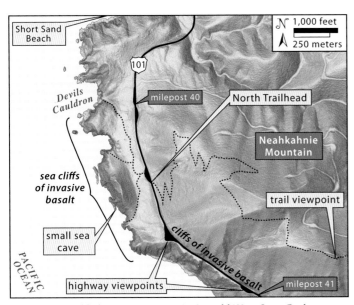

Neahkahnie Mountain is in Oswald West State Park north of Nehalem Bay.

Sea cave eroded along fractures in the invasive basalt. Cape Falcon in the distance.

View north to Hug Point, the second headland north of the parking area, with Tillamook Head in the distance. Note the basalt sill and alcove in the first headland on the right.

 HUG POINT STATE RECREATION SITE
Invasive Basalt and Contorted Sandstone

At medium to low tides, you can walk miles on the beach by Hug Point, located just over 4 miles south of Cannon Beach on US 101. Its sea cliffs display wonderful exposures of the Astoria Formation and its relations to invasive sills and dikes of the Grande Ronde Basalt. Probably the most accessible exposures of the basalt are in the small headlands immediately north and south of the parking lot. If you go south, look for a pair of dikes as well as a sill of the basalt. Just north of the parking lot, you can't miss the narrow sill that extends diagonally up from a wave-eroded alcove. Walk around this small headland to see a much larger intrusion that connects with the sill. One of its sides is faulted and eroded into a small sea cave.

Hug Point, the second headland north of the parking area, protrudes far enough into the surf that you practically need to hug the rocks to get around, hence its name. In the late 1800s travelers carved a road along the cliff base so they could pass relatively easily at low tide. Sandstone of the Astoria Formation along this stretch contains mostly large grains of quartz and feldspar. You can also see abundant cross bedding from deposition by currents, as well as rip-up clasts, where storms eroded the underlying bed and included parts of it within the newly deposited light-colored sand. This coarse-grained part of the Astoria Formation, called the Angora Peak Member, was deposited on a delta that was continually affected by waves and storms of the Miocene ocean. The rock layers tilt gently northeastward toward younger rocks.

A cliff of highly contorted sandstone lies immediately north of Hug Point. The irregular nature of the folding

Main sources and further reading: Beeson and others, 1979; Cooper, 1980; Niem, 1975

suggests that deformation occurred while the Astoria Formation was still soft. Given the abundance of the basaltic intrusions here, geologists interpret the cause of this folding to be related to the intrusions. Another quarter mile to the north, highly fragmented sandstone and basalt are mixed together, likely the product of the explosions that resulted during the basalt intrusions.

In another mile north of Hug Point, you reach Lion Rock and Humbug Point—where the Astoria Formation shows more interaction with the basalt—and another half mile beyond that, Silver Point. There, a cliff exposes shale of the Astoria Formation's Silver Point Member, deposited in a deeper part of the delta complex. Because these rocks sit on top of the coarser Angora Peak Member and are therefore younger, they suggest that the delta was subsiding through time. And if you want to keep walking, Cannon Beach's Haystack Rock is just another 2 miles to the north.

Contorted bedding of the Astoria Formation in the cliffs just north of Hug Point.

Looking southward along the stretch of old roadway carved into the cliffs at Hug Point. The sandstone here contains cross bedding, rip-up clasts, and even some small faults.

③ HAYSTACK ROCK AT CANNON BEACH
Submarine Volcano Erupted Eastern Oregon Lava

Haystack Rock at Cannon Beach is no ordinary sea stack. Like all sea stacks, it's composed of rock more resistant to weathering and erosion than the surrounding rock, which has since been eroded. But unlike other sea stacks, Haystack Rock was an undersea volcano whose magma erupted for a second time! Its magma came from surface lavas of the Wanapum Basalt, which originated as fissure eruptions between 15.6 and 15 million years ago in eastern Oregon and flowed all the way to the sea. The lava at the base of the surface flows was under considerable pressure, so it injected downward into recently deposited sediments of the Astoria Formation and formed a shallow magma chamber that erupted undersea.

Geologists who mapped the sea stack found pillow basalt and fragments of Astoria Formation that were torn off the seafloor during the eruptions. They also found basaltic dikes and sills that intruded the volcanic complex and fed its eruptions. Next to the main sea stack are smaller sea stacks called the Needles that formed as feeder dikes splitting off from the main volcano. You can approach Haystack Rock at low tide, but you are not allowed to climb on it because it is a protected national wildlife area for nesting seabirds.

Haystack Rock consists of a variety of rock types, including pillow basalt, basaltic breccia, sandstone of the Astoria Formation, and dikes and sills of invasive basalt.

View southward of Haystack Rock and the Needles. The town of Cannon Beach, not visible in photo, occupies the coastal area.

Main source and further reading: Wells and others, 2009

THREE CAPES LOOP
A Tour of Meares, Lookout, and Kiwanda

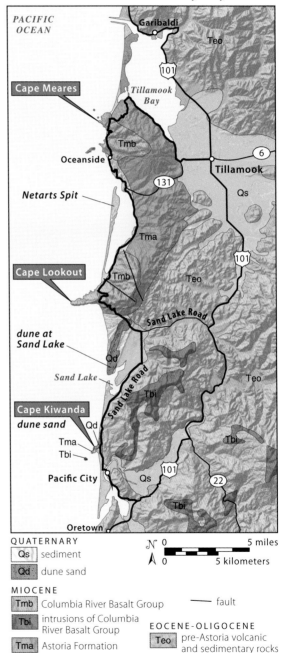

Three Capes Loop provides leisurely access to three capes, while US 101 takes a more direct route between Tillamook and Pacific City.

Between Tillamook and Pacific City, three prominent headlands dominate the coastal landscape: Capes Meares, Lookout, and Kiwanda. Each is easily accessible by roads of the Three Capes Loop, a scenic tour that joins US 101 at Tillamook and again just north of the town of Oretown. Along the way, you can see Grande Ronde Basalt and the sedimentary rock it intruded and flowed over, along with plenty of sand.

Cape Meares beautifully displays multiple flows of Grande Ronde Basalt. The lowest exposed flows contain pillows and breccias, which indicate the lava poured into the ocean. Higher flows display a colonnade—vertical columns of basalt—which indicate they cooled on land. Near the top of the sequence, a bright-red zone marks an ancient soil that formed on the underlying flow during a volcanically quiet time. Some yellowish sedimentary rocks on top of the lava were deposited during the period between eruptions of the Grande Ronde and Wanapum Basalts. The best view of these cliffs is from an overlook about halfway along the trail from the parking lot to the lighthouse. If you look southward along the coastline, you can see a line of sea stacks near Oceanside that also eroded from lavas of the Grande Ronde Basalt.

Cape Lookout forms a narrow peninsula that juts 2 miles straight out from the coastline, more than any other headland in Oregon. Even more enigmatic, it originated as a river valley in Miocene time. The valley filled with lava of the Grande Ronde Basalt, which was far more resistant to erosion than the valley walls. Over time, erosion removed the valley walls, leaving the more resistant lava flow standing as a ridge.

The beach on the cape's south side, accessed by a steep trail, offers spectacular views of the flows that formed the cape, including a thick flow of pillow basalt as well as some colonnade. Many of the fallen blocks contain large gas bubbles, some of which are filled with zeolite minerals and others with agate. An outstanding exposure of Astoria Formation, which formed the bedrock of the original valley, lies about one-third mile along the headland. To visit it, make sure the tide is not rising. Another trail leads through old growth forest of Sitka spruce to the end of the cape with occasional views southward.

Netarts Spit, extending more than 4 miles north from the northern base of Cape Lookout, offers another enigma. Its orientation

QUATERNARY
Qs sediment
Qd dune sand

MIOCENE
Tmb Columbia River Basalt Group
Tbi intrusions of Columbia River Basalt Group
Tma Astoria Formation

— fault

EOCENE-OLIGOCENE
Teo pre-Astoria volcanic and sedimentary rocks

15

View of lava flows in the northernmost headland of Cape Meares. The pillows are in the flow at the very bottom near the point. Several flows higher up display a colonnade.

View of the basalt flows that form Cape Lookout, as seen from the beach on its south side. Inset shows the bedrock exposure of Astoria Formation that formed the walls of the ancient valley down which the lava flowed.

Cape Kiwanda, made mostly of Astoria Formation, and its protective haystack rock of invasive basalt.

indicates northward drift of sand, driven largely by south-westerly winds during winter storms. However, by sticking so far out to sea, Cape Lookout prevents migration of sand from any source to the south. Geologists surmise that the sand moved northward during the Pleistocene Epoch, when sea level was lower and the coastline lay some 15 to 20 miles to the west, beyond the reach of the Cape Lookout headland. Then, as sea level rose, the sand migrated eastward onto today's shoreline.

Unlike regular headlands formed of resistant rock, Cape Kiwanda is composed of such easily eroded Astoria Formation that hikers are no longer allowed to explore the cliff tops. It forms a headland because it's protected by the prominent haystack rock just offshore, composed of resistant invasive lavas of the Grande Ronde Basalt. Some great sedimentary rock exposures, however, are easily accessed along the base of the cliffs on the cape's south side. Beginning next to the beach, you can see the Oligocene Alsea Formation, which erodes even more easily than the overlying Astoria. Some normal faults visibly offset the contact between the Alsea and Astoria Formations. A little farther southwest along the cliffs, a basaltic dike intrudes the Astoria Formation. This dike belongs to the Grande Ronde Basalt, the same invasive lavas that form the prominent haystack rock a half-mile offshore.

The giant sand dune on the northern edge of Cape Kiwanda has its own story. It once blanketed the cape, but erosion partially removed it to expose the bedrock below. You can find ancient soil horizons in the nearby dunes. Radiometric dating of the soils near the bottom of the dunes indicate they formed about 7,000 years ago; those near the top of the dunes are as young as 350 years old.

Main sources and further reading: Beeson and others, 1979; Clemens and Komar, 1988; Cooper, 1958; Komar, 1997; Peterson and others, 2007; Wells and others, 1994

5 SADDLE MOUNTAIN STATE NATURAL AREA
Basaltic Breccia That Filled a Submarine Canyon

At an elevation of 3,288 feet, Saddle Mountain is the highest point in Oregon's Clatsop County and one of the highest peaks in the northern Coast Range. The mountain consists entirely of basaltic breccia, or fragments of angular basalt. Basaltic dikes intrude the breccia in many places. A trail passes many outstanding rock exposures as it leads 3 miles and 1,600 feet vertically up to the summit. The Humbug Mountain Viewpoint, a 40-foot-high knob of basaltic breccia only a half mile from the parking lot, provides the best spot to view Saddle Mountain in its entirety.

Lava flows of the Grande Ronde Basalt erupted between 16 and 15.6 million years ago from fissures in eastern Oregon and flowed west. On reaching the shoreline, which lay much farther inland in Miocene time (nearly to Portland, Oregon), the lava and water interacted explosively to form a crust of breccia beneath which more lava flowed. Farther out to sea, in the vicinity of today's Saddle Mountain, the lava poured down a submarine canyon. Each time a pulse of lava broke out from its protective crust, it contacted the seawater to form volcanic glass and pillow basalt, exploding

Summit area of Saddle Mountain as seen from the Humbug Mountain Viewpoint. Note the visible basaltic dike.

To reach the trailhead, take US 26 to a quarter mile east of milepost 10 and then head north for 7 miles on the marked road to the Saddle Mountain State Natural Area.

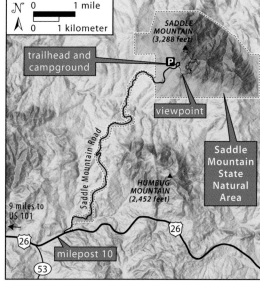

Main sources and further reading: Beeson and others, 1979; Wells and others, 1979

and fragmenting at the same time. Much of the volcanic glass reacted with the seawater to form palagonite, the brown-colored material that forms much of the matrix that holds the breccia together.

The dikes of Saddle Mountain formed when portions of the flowing lava worked their way upward along cracks in the protective crust. You can see several of these dikes in the southwestern face of Saddle Mountain and along the trail. At the top of Saddle Mountain, you gain a sweeping view of the region. Looking southwestward toward the coast, you see the path of the submarine canyon, now expressed as Humbug and Sugarloaf Mountains and Onion Peak, all composed of similar basaltic breccia.

Fragmented pillow basalt in a matrix of broken basalt and palagonite—typical basaltic breccia of Saddle Mountain.

View southwestward over a basaltic dike (light rock in center) toward Humbug Mountain (on the left) and Sugarloaf Mountain and Onion Peak (in the background).

Humbug Mountain **Onion Peak** **Sugarloaf Mountain**

GHOST FOREST AT NESKOWIN
Sitka Spruce Drowned by an Earthquake

At low tide, the beach at Neskowin beautifully displays hundreds of drowned trees, now barren stumps, emerging from the sand. They likely drowned during an earthquake along the Cascadia subduction zone about 1,600 years ago. Earthquakes along the Pacific coast release an immense amount of energy, built up during the period before the earthquake. Much of this energy is stored in the land as it gradually rises out of the surf zone, to be colonized by plants and even forests if given enough time. Similar to an elastic band that slowly stretched to its breaking point, breakage along the subduction zone causes it to slip and release its energy. When it does, the land subsides back into the surf zone and the forest drowns.

Using the ages of the many other ghost forests, subsided marsh deposits, and tsunami (large sea wave) deposits up and down the coast, researchers have documented at least a dozen other earthquakes along the Cascadia subduction zone over the past 7,000 years. The most recent event corresponded to a tsunami that reached Japan in January 1700. By backtracking the arrival time of the tsunami, researchers estimated the earthquake to the hour: about 9 p.m. Pacific Standard Time, on January 26.

To see the Neskowin ghost forest, park at the Neskowin Beach State Recreation Site, a quarter mile north of milepost 98, and follow the trail to the beach, wading across Neskowin Creek if passable (typically during summer months only). The stumps are mostly at the far south end of the beach. Proposal Rock, a large sea stack of Oligocene-age basalt, reaches upward some 50 feet just north of the stumps. If you are unable to wade across Neskowin Creek, two stumps poke through the creek on the north side of Proposal Rock.

View northward over drowned trees toward Proposal Rock.
Inset: Close-up view of preserved wood in a drowned tree.

Main sources and further reading: Hart, 1997; Peterson and others, 1993

View north along Devils Punchbowl beach to the uplifted marine terrace. Tilted Astoria Formation forms the gray cliffs beneath the cream-colored, 125,000- to 80,000-year-old terrace sediment.

DEVILS PUNCHBOWL STATE NATURAL AREA
Uplift and Erosion of the Astoria Formation

When it comes to the three geologic elements that give character to Oregon beaches—great rocks, coastal uplift, and erosion—Devils Punchbowl is certainly one of the best. In addition to the circular punchbowl, a collapsed sea cave, the half-mile stretch of beach immediately to the north offers tilted sedimentary rocks, invasive lava flows, normal faults, an uplifted marine terrace, sea stacks, and land-slides. At low tide, you can explore wonderful tidepools and access the 85-foot-wide, 50-foot-deep Punchbowl itself. As the ocean surf erodes the base of cliffs, it can form deep caverns that flood during high tide. At Devils Punchbowl, the roof collapsed, exposing the sea cave.

The rocks are mostly sandstones of the Astoria Formation, deposited in a delta and shallow ocean between about 20 to 15 million years ago during the early Miocene Epoch. Because they are tilted, you walk northward into younger rocks, which become finer grained and more thinly bedded to suggest the Miocene ocean water became deeper over time. In many places within the rock, you can find small deposits of broken clam shells, likely stirred up and scattered during storms. On the southern edge of the first headland to the north, you can see evidence of submarine slumping in the form of irregular folds in the rock.

Dikes of Columbia River Basalt Group intrude the sandstone. You can see a dike and sill next to the waterfall north of the first headland, as well as some car-sized blocks of basaltic breccia. The breccias likely formed during explosions as the hot lava interacted with the wet sediment.

Main sources and further reading: Beeson and others, 1979; Cooper, 1980

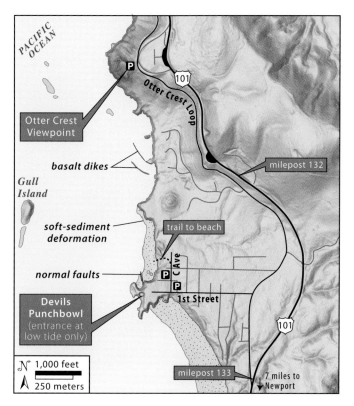

Devils Punchbowl State Natural Area is accessed from the small town of Otter Rock, about 8 miles north of Newport.

At low tide, you can look down on the beach from Otter Crest Viewpoint (about 1 mile north of Devils Punchbowl) and see two long arcuate dikes extending offshore.

A marine terrace of 125,000- to 80,000-year-old sediment deposited on top of the older rock lies about 75 feet above the beach. Because this younger sediment accumulated at sea level, it speaks to very recent uplift along the coastline. Expressions of older periods of uplift are seen in the tilted sandstone beds themselves because they originated as a series of horizontal sheets of sediment below sea level. There are also a number of normal faults that offset these beds, moving the block beneath the fault up relative to the block above the fault. The breakage along faults naturally enhances weathering and erosion. Near the opening to the Punchbowl, look for a small sea cave that formed along the trace of one of the faults.

View south from Otter Crest Viewpoint of arcuate-shaped dikes and Devils Punchbowl. Most of the buildings occupy the flat, uplifted terrace.

Deformation in the Astoria Formation occurred while the sediment was still soft.

Devils Punchbowl, a collapsed sea cave in the Astoria Formation, as seen from the overlook on top the marine terrace.

8 YAQUINA HEAD NATURAL OUTSTANDING AREA
An Inverted River Valley

Prior to 15 million years ago, Yaquina Head was a valley, eroded into sedimentary rocks of the Miocene Astoria Formation. Then, lavas of the Wanapum Basalt flowed down the valley and into the ocean. Through time, some of the basalt and most of the softer Astoria Formation eroded

Look for the turnoff to Yaquina Head 2.7 miles north of Newport on US 101.

away, leaving the lava flow standing as a ridge that now forms one of the most prominent basaltic headlands on Oregon's coast. Sandstone of the Astoria Formation shows up along the shoreline on either side of the basalt to mark what remains of the original valley. The same flows of Wanapum Basalt also show up east of the Coast Range near Salem. Researchers suggest these lavas, also called the Basalt of Ginkgo, flowed across what is now the Coast Range to the Newport area but were eroded from the mountains as the Coast Range was uplifted.

Some of the lavas at Yaquina Head show evidence that they reached the sea, while others seem to have cooled on land. Those that flowed into water are highly fragmented and contain the brown mineral palagonite, which forms by the interaction of water and hot volcanic glass. Some of the best examples of these palagonite breccias are on Cobble Beach, where you might also find some broken pillow lavas. Wave action at Cobble Beach wore broken fragments of basalt into nearly spherical pebbles and cobbles.

The headland, now managed as the Yaquina Head Outstanding Natural Area by the Bureau of Land Management, offers numerous opportunities for observing these rocks up close and seeing evidence for coastal uplift. Its visitor center and bookstore lie within the upper of two rock quarries, active from 1917 through the 1970s, which produced crushed basalt used for local road construction. Quarry Cove,

Aerial view looking southeast over the resistant basalt of Yaquina Head. The tan-colored bluffs on the north (left) side of the photo are sandstone of the Astoria Formation. The lighthouse is 93 feet tall.

Main sources and further reading: Beeson and others, 1979; Mardock, 1994; Reidel and others, 2013

Nearly spherical cobbles of basalt rest on an outcrop of palagonite breccia at Cobble Beach.

the lower quarry, is flooded at high tides and hosts outstanding tidepools. Both quarries offer views of lava that cooled on land, with beautiful examples of the entablature—the closely spaced, mostly vertical but irregular fracturing in the rock. Other indications of land-based cooling consist of a few small examples of the colonnade, the thicker, more regular variety of columnar jointing, and some reported examples of the angular aa lava and the ropy-textured pahoehoe lava, both of which form on land.

The Yaquina Head lighthouse, at 93 feet, is the tallest lighthouse in Oregon and the third tallest on the west coast. It sits atop an uplifted marine terrace that formed at sea level about 80,000 years ago. Accompanying the uplift, windblown sand accumulated over much of the basalt. You can easily see the sand near the visitor center. Also accompanying the uplift was more erosion. Looking over the edge of the headland, you can see how it is eroding, leaving behind some of the more resistant rock as sea stacks.

Outcrop of Astoria Formation with the basalt of Yaquina Head in the background.

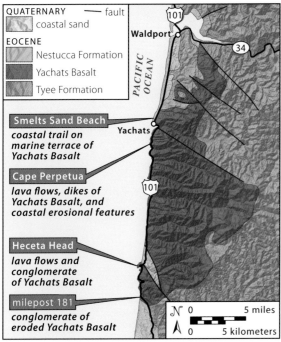

PACIFIC OCEAN

Waldport

Yachats

Smelts Sand Beach
coastal trail on marine terrace of Yachats Basalt

Cape Perpetua
lava flows, dikes of Yachats Basalt, and coastal erosional features

Heceta Head
lava flows and conglomerate of Yachats Basalt

milepost 181
conglomerate of eroded Yachats Basalt

N   0   5 miles
     0   5 kilometers

The dramatic Cape Perpetua coastline begins about 9 miles north of Florence.

9 YACHATS BASALT OF CAPE PERPETUA
Lava from Ancient Shield Volcanoes

The Yachats Basalt forms one of Oregon's most spectacular stretches of coastline: a 13-mile-long series of headlands and beaches from north of Florence to the town of Yachats. The basalt's natural resistance to erosion allows it to persist in places, even under the crushing power of ocean waves, to form prominent headlands, several of which protrude well into the ocean and drop precipitously to the waves below. Cape Perpetua forms the highest, and arguably most interesting, headland in the group.

The Yachats Basalt originated as a complex of shield volcanoes between about 36 and 34 million years ago in late Eocene time. The rocks reach a thickness of nearly 2,500 feet in places and show evidence of erupting underwater as well as on land. Near its northern and southern edges at Yachats and Heceta Head, respectively, basaltic conglomerates can be found among the lava flows, evidence that erosion removed, rounded, and deposited boulders of basalt during the life of the volcanoes.

The Cape Perpetua Scenic Area offers well-exposed lava flows and dikes of the complex. Individual flows are particularly obvious on the steep southern face below the lookout, which reaches an elevation just above 800 feet. Along the coastline, you can clamber over individual flows, most of which are 5 to 10 feet thick. Several contain breccias along their bases that grade upward into denser interiors and smooth upper surfaces, similar to lava flows that form on land today. Numerous dikes cut through these flows and likely fed the eruption of younger flows. If you look closely, you can see

View southward at low tide along the coastline of the Yachats Basalt as seen from the viewpoint atop Cape Perpetua. The flat surface on the black rock is the bench eroded in the basalt. The light-colored sediment that overlies the bench has been uplifted since it formed at or below the waves.

chilled margins—where the dikes cooled against the already-cooled lava flows—and even baked zones, where the hot intruding dikes heated the older flows.

Much of the walkable part of the coastline at Cape Perpetua consists of a bench that now sits a few feet above high tide. Similar to the wave-cut bench at Sunset Bay (site 13), it formed just below the base of ocean waves and has since been uplifted to its present elevation. Along the landward edge of the bench, you can see overlying light-colored sediments that were deposited at or below sea level.

Some of the more popular places at Cape Perpetua formed from erosion into this uplifted bench. At Devils Churn and Cooks Chasm, the roiling surf rushes up a narrow channel eroded into the bedrock and crashes against a steep wall at the back. The Spouting Horn, which lies toward the back of Cooks Chasm, is eroded so that the incoming wave launches high into the air. Thors Well, another popular place, is a partially collapsed roof of a sea cave.

A conglomerate composed of basaltic boulders at Heceta Head.

At Thors Well, incoming swells surge up through the roof in the collapsed sea cave and drain back downward.

10 MARYS PEAK
Siletzia of the Coast Range

On clear days, you can see the Pacific Ocean from the top of Marys Peak—and if you look eastward, you can see several of the Cascade volcanoes. As the highest peak in the Oregon Coast Range with an elevation of 4,097 feet, Marys Peak soars over its surrounding landscape. Its stunning topographic relief results from a cap of resistant rock with an unusual story.

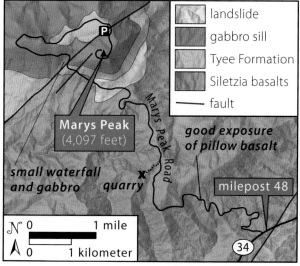

landslide
gabbro sill
Tyee Formation
Siletzia basalts
— fault

Marys Peak (4,097 feet)

Marys Peak Road

small waterfall and gabbro

quarry ✗

good exposure of pillow basalt

milepost 48

34

N 0   1 mile
0   1 kilometer

To reach Marys Peak from Corvallis, head west on US 20 for 6 miles, then turn south on OR 34 and drive 9 miles. Turn right on Marys Peak Road just west of milepost 48.

The top 1,000 feet of Marys Peak is composed of gabbro, an intrusive igneous rock relatively poor in silica and rich in iron when compared to a granite. Because it tends to resist erosion, it forms numerous prominent ridgelines and peaks in the Coast Range, and even waterfalls like Sweet Creek Falls (site 11). About 32 million years ago, the gabbro intruded older rock of the Coast Range. At Marys Peak, this older rock consists of submarine basalt of Siletzia, which accreted to North America about 50 million years ago, and overlying sandstone and shale of the Tyee Formation, deposited after Siletzia was accreted.

The basalt, which is also resistant to erosion, forms a ramp that tilts upward from the Willamette Valley toward and beyond Marys Peak. The tilted platform of resistant basalt supports the more-resistant gabbro in its lofty position atop the Coast Range.

You can see exposures of the Siletzia basalt, Tyee Formation, and gabbro by driving the 9.1 miles up the paved but steep road on Marys Peak and then walking the half mile to its summit. At 3.3 miles up the road, look for some beautiful pillow basalt in the roadcut on the right side of the road. At 5.0 miles, you can park and walk a quarter mile to an abandoned quarry that hosts some even better exposures. At 6.1 miles, you pass some outstanding exposures of the Tyee Formation, and at 7.5 miles, near a small waterfall along a fault zone, you encounter the gabbro. Good outcrops of the gabbro also line the access road at the top of the peak.

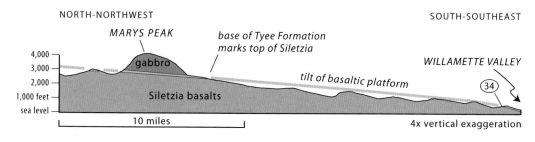

NORTH-NORTHWEST

MARYS PEAK

base of Tyee Formation marks top of Siletzia

SOUTH-SOUTHEAST

4,000
3,000
2,000
1,000 feet
sea level

gabbro

WILLAMETTE VALLEY

tilt of basaltic platform

34

Siletzia basalts

10 miles

4x vertical exaggeration

Cross section of Marys Peak, showing the north-northeastward tilt of the basaltic platform that forms the erosional top of Siletzia. The gabbro intruded along the top of Siletzia, with a narrow band of Tyee Formation between them. The erosionally resistant gabbro now forms the main edifice of Marys Peak.

Main sources and further reading: Baldwin, 1955; Oxford, 2006; Wells and others, 2014

Aerial view of Marys Peak (highest on right) and nearby mountains of the Coast Range.

Outcrop of gabbro at the top of Marys Peak. Inset shows close-up view of gabbro. Because it cooled slowly at depth, it has mineral crystals large enough to see without magnification.

11 SWEET CREEK FALLS
Different Rocks, Different Waterfalls

Few places give as satisfying a feeling for the Oregon Coast Range as the short hike along Sweet Creek near Mapleton. The trail passes four waterfalls that dramatically illustrate the different styles of erosion between sedimentary and intrusive igneous rock. The sedimentary rock is sandstone of the Tyee Formation, deposited on the ocean bottom in a submarine fan complex some 45 million years ago during the Eocene Epoch. The igneous rock is gabbro, which intruded much of the Coast Range, including the top of Marys Peak (site 10), between 33 and 32 million years ago.

The 1-mile hike to the upper falls passes mostly through outcrops of the gabbro with a few hundred yards of Tyee outcrops near the middle of the hike. Where the creek is flowing through the gabbro, you see an unpredictable arrangement of waterfalls and steep cascades. Where it's flowing over the sandstone, the creek takes a gentler gradient, with nearly flat stretches broken by short cascades where the water spills over ledges.

The reason for these differences lies in the nature of the rocks. Gabbro, having cooled slowly underground from a liquid state, is naturally homogeneous except where it's broken by fractures, which tend to run in several different directions. River erosion of the gabbro exploits the fractures to create narrow, steep, somewhat unpredictable passageways for the water. By contrast, the sandstone contains consistently horizontal bedding planes. The more resistant beds form the nearly flat bottoms of the channel, which tend to end abruptly at small steps where the water cascades downward to another resistant bed.

To reach the Sweet Creek Falls Trailhead, take Sweet Creek Road (5036) south for 10 miles from OR 126 at Mapleton (which is 14 miles east of US 101 at Florence).

Hiker and walkway overlooking a tributary creek, just above Annice Falls. The rock here is gabbro.

Main source and further reading: Baldwin, 1956

At Elk Wallow Falls, about halfway from the parking lot to Sweet Creek Falls, the creek spills over ledges of 45-million-year-old Tyee Formation.

Sweet Creek Falls flows over 32- to 33-million-year-old gabbro of the Coast Range. Rounded, moss-covered rocks in the foreground are also gabbro.

31

View southward over the northern extent of the Coos Bay dune field, about 6 miles north of Florence.

12 COOS BAY DUNE FIELD
Endless Sand from Pleistocene Time

Sand dunes of varying sizes decorate about 45 percent of Oregon's coastline. The Coos Bay dune field, which stretches nearly 60 miles from Coos Bay to north of Florence, is one of the largest continuous sheets of sand on North America's West Coast. Much of the Coos Bay dune field begins with low, grass-covered foredunes next to the beach, a low-lying deflation plain just inland, and larger dunes beyond that. The deflation plain, where wind erosion largely removed the sand down to the water table, is marked by numerous swampy areas, ponds, and locally thick stands of water-loving vegetation. These areas have grown considerably since European beach grass was planted in the early 1900s to stabilize the foredunes. The stabilization was so successful that the foredunes no longer replenish the areas behind them with sand.

The larger inland dunes reach heights greater than 150 feet. These dunes form oblique to the coastline, shaped by a combination of the two prevailing wind directions: northerly winds during the summer and more variable but generally southwesterly winds during the winter. Smaller transverse dunes form perpendicular to the northerly winds and get smoothed over by the winter winds. Numerous isolated clumps of coastal forest mark areas that have not been completely inundated by the moving sand, while lakes form where moving sand dams local drainages.

The dune sand contains a small amount of the minerals glaucophane and pink garnet, neither of which is found in the Coast Range or Cascades. Instead, these minerals formed in some of the metamorphic rocks of the Klamath Mountains of southern Oregon and northern California. This observation creates a problem, however, as the numerous headlands between the Klamath Mountains and the Coos Bay dune field would preclude northward transport of the sand.

 Main sources and further reading: Clemens and Komar, 1988; Cooper, 1958; Komar, 1997; Peterson and others, 2007

The solution to the problem also may explain why the Coos Bay dune field is so gigantic. During the lower sea levels of the Pleistocene Epoch, when water was tied up in massive continental ice sheets, the coastline lay some tens of miles farther west. Only one major headland protruded into the sea. You can see this headland, now the submerged Heceta Bank offshore from Yachats, in the bathymetric map of the seafloor. Most northward migrating sand during Pleistocene time piled up on the south side of Heceta Bank. Some of the sand blew onshore and is preserved today as older dunes, but even more moved shoreward during sea level rise after the Pleistocene ended to become the modern dunes.

Most of the dunes lie within the Oregon Dunes National Recreation Area, managed by the Siuslaw National Forest. They allow ATV use in about half the area and reserve half for hikers only. Some beach areas are closed during spring and summer to protect the snowy plover, a small shorebird that builds its nests on open beach sand. You can access the dunes from nearly all the state parks and campgrounds along the coast between Florence and Coos Bay.

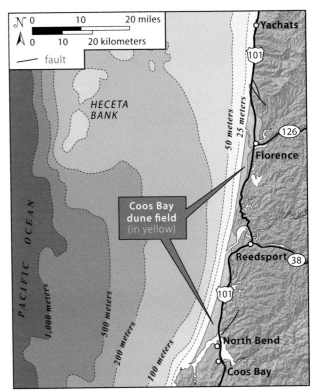

Map of the Coos Bay dune field and seafloor bathymetry. The dunes are in yellow. —Bathymetry from NOAA Office of Coast Survey, US Bathymetric and Fishing maps

At the eroded coastal edge of the dunes, you can see horizontal layers and cross bedding. European beach grass covers the crest of the dunes.

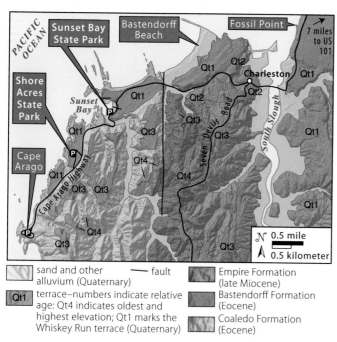

	sand and other alluvium (Quaternary)	— fault		Empire Formation (late Miocene)
Qt1	terrace–numbers indicate relative age: Qt4 indicates oldest and highest elevation; Qt1 marks the Whiskey Run terrace (Quaternary)			Bastendorff Formation (Eocene)
				Coaledo Formation (Eocene)

To reach Sunset Bay, head west from Coos Bay to the small town of Charleston and then follow the Cape Arago Highway 2.7 miles. Shore Acres is less than another mile along the road. Qt1 marks the Whiskey Run terrace, the youngest of several uplifted marine terraces.

⬣13 SUNSET BAY AND SHORE ACRES STATE PARKS
Wave-Cut Platforms and Uplifted Terraces

The reason Sunset Bay State Park has such wonderful tide-pools is because the surf's erosive action planed off the rocks into a wave-cut platform. While most of the flat platform surface is exposed and accessible at low tides, numerous deeper pools remain submerged, hosting a wide variety of colorful and fascinating sea creatures. Waves excavated the pools by eroding along the steeply inclined bedding.

The rock consists of the Coaledo Formation, deposited between 44 and 40 million years ago during the Eocene Epoch. The unit is named for coal seams it contains elsewhere, suggesting it was deposited in a large delta—and the variety of features at Sunset Bay, including ripple marks, cross bedding, and some marine fossils, support this interpretation. Besides their steep angles, the rocks at Sunset Bay are offset by strike-slip faults in several places, reflecting some of the later deformation that has taken place along the Oregon Coast.

Although frequently covered by sand, ancient tree trunks can sometimes be seen in the surf zone on the south side of Sunset Bay. These trunks drowned from coastal subsidence during an earthquake about 1,100 years ago, similar to what happened at Neskowin (site 6) but at a different time. Farther out on the platform, you can also see some beautiful honeycomb shapes in the Coaledo Formation. Salt, carried by ocean spray, gets deposited on the rock and soaks into its pores, where it precipitates and crystallizes to cause microcracking and enlargement of the pore spaces. These tiny cavities can then collect more spray and salt, leading to further enlargement.

The flat surface at the top of the 20-foot-high cliffs around Sunset Bay mark an older wave-cut platform, buried by coastal sand and gravel and uplifted to its present position. Called the Whiskey Run terrace, it's about 80,000 years old. You can walk around on the terrace at Shore Acres State Park, only 1 mile south. The Whiskey Run terrace lies at a slightly higher elevation at Shore Acres than at Sunset Bay because the uplift also involved some gentle folding; the terrace slopes down to the north and disappears beneath South Slough at the town of Charleston, then slopes back up to the surface toward the north. Four older terraces, perched at progressively higher elevations, have been identified in the vicinity.

From the edge of the terrace at Shore Acres, you can look down to see how the waves erode the steeply inclined Coaledo Formation below. Preferential erosion of the softer beds leaves ridges of more resistant rock separating narrow, water-filled chasms. You also can see thousands of concretions, which look like bowling balls emerging from the rock. They form because groundwater precipitates minerals that cement more resistant zones in the rock. The precipitation likely starts at an irregularity in the rock, such as a shell fragment, and expands outward in all directions. The concretions stand out as roughly spherical shapes because the less-resistant parts of the rock weather away.

Main sources and further reading: Armentrout, 1980; Baldwin and Beaulieu, 1973; Hart, 1997; Prothero and Donohoo, 2001

Wave-cut bench at Sunset Bay, with strike-slip faults offsetting the steeply tilted bedding in the Coaledo Formation.

Tilted Coaledo Formation at Shore Acres State Park with forest developed on the uplifted Whiskey Run terrace. Several concretions stand out from the sandstone cliff on the right side of the photo like irregular bowling balls.

Close-up of some faults and fractures cutting cross-bedded sandstone of the Coaledo Formation at Sunset Bay. Photo view is about 3 feet across.

35

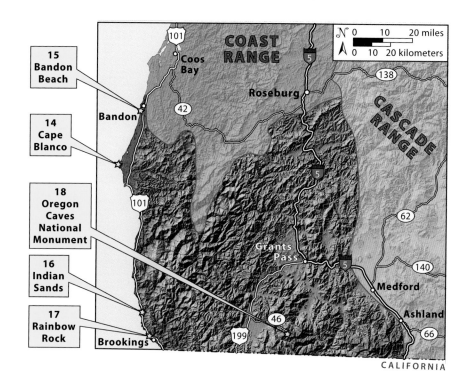

KLAMATH MOUNTAINS

Occupying the southwestern corner of Oregon, the Klamath Mountains form a virtual maze of steep canyons and ridges, drained by the Rogue River in Oregon and the Klamath River in northern California. The bedrock, which here includes the Franciscan Complex along the coast, consists almost entirely of terranes accreted at various times during the Mesozoic Era. These terranes include slices of oceanic lithosphere as well as rock of the mantle, called peridotite, much of which has been metamorphosed to the rock serpentinite. These iron- and nickel-rich rocks provide targets for mining but also host unusual vegetation types.

The Franciscan Complex, the youngest part of the Klamaths, formed in oceanic settings such as island arcs, marine plateaus, or as deep ocean sediment during the late Jurassic through middle Cretaceous Period. The variety of rock became highly deformed and mixed together on coming together in a subduction zone and is called mélange. The four coastal sites described here formed on three separate

terranes within the Franciscan Complex and show great differences between them. Bandon Beach offers sea stacks and stranded blocks that range from sandstone to serpentinite; Cape Blanco and Indian Sands feature the Jurassic Otter Point Formation, a variety of sedimentary rock deposited mostly in the deep ocean; and Rainbow Rock consists of colorful, folded chert.

The accreted terranes also host rock deposited in a shallow sea, such as limestone that was later metamorphosed to the marble of Oregon Caves. Numerous stitching plutons, including the Grayback pluton next to Oregon Caves, as well as the Ashland and Grants Pass plutons, intrude the terranes. As these plutons cooled and crystallized, between about 140 and 100 million years ago, they generated hydrothermal fluids that precipitated gold and a variety of other valuable metals. In many ways, the Klamaths resemble the Blue Mountains geologically except the terranes in the Blue Mountains are more obscured by overlying rock units.

View southeastward from near the lighthouse at Cape Blanco. Terrace gravels cap the light-colored Empire Formation in the foreground. The dark rock at center is the Otter Point Formation, which forms a headland. Beyond it is the sloping landslide area and Needle Rock, made of conglomerate of the Sandstone of Floras Lake.

CAPE BLANCO
Oregon's Westernmost Point

Named for its white cliffs of Miocene sandstone, Cape Blanco forms Oregon's westernmost point. Its flat surface, some 200 feet above the waves, hosts Oregon's longest continuously operational lighthouse, built in 1870. From the parking lot about a quarter mile east of the lighthouse, you can see that gravel forms the flat surface. It was deposited at sea level about 80,000 years ago on top of a wave-eroded bedrock platform, similar to the wave-cut bench at Sunset Bay (site 13) or Bandon (site 15). Now a marine terrace, it has since been uplifted to its present elevation. This surface, called the Cape Blanco terrace is approximately the same age as the Whiskey Run terrace to the north. The edge of the gravel terrace deposit forms a small cliff, or

headwall, above a landslide—and you can see places along the cliff edge starting to give way.

Continuing to the lighthouse from the first parking lot, the road dips below the terrace and follows a ridge narrowed by landslides on both sides. Easily eroded gray shale and sandstone of the Umpqua Group, deposited in the deep ocean during the Eocene, are prone to landslides. Look for some poor exposures of these rocks within the slides.

You can reach the sea cliffs along Cape Blanco's south side by following the campground road to a small parking area just above the beach. Pleistocene river and shallow ocean deposits of the Port Orford Formation form the cliffs south of the road and Miocene shallow ocean deposits form

Main sources and further reading: Armentrout, 1980; Dott, 1971; Kelsey, 1990

Pleistocene river gravel of the Port Orford Formation lies on top of the Miocene Empire Formation at the campground's beach access.

Looking west toward the lighthouse across the upper reaches of a landslide. At right is the 80,000-year-old gravel deposit that caps the Cape Blanco terrace.

the cliffs to the north. The Miocene Sandstone of Floras Lake and overlying Empire Formation, deposited from about 18 to 5 million years ago, tilt southward, so you walk into progressively older rock as you walk north up the beach. Needle Rock, a sea stack near the north end of the beach, is conglomerate and sandstone of the Sandstone of Floras Lake. A small headland of gray, Jurassic-age Otter Point Formation forms the north end of the beach, positioned against the younger rocks along a fault zone. At very low tides, you can walk around the headland to the down-dropped side of this fault and find the younger Empire Formation deposited directly on the Otter Point Formation with no intervening Umpqua Group or Sandstone of Floras Lake. Its absence likely reflects erosion of the uplifted side of the fault before the Empire Formation was deposited.

The Miocene-age, light-colored Empire Formation was deposited on top of the dark, Jurassic-age Otter Point Formation on the southwest edge of Cape Blanco. Here, there is no intervening Sandstone of Floras Lake.

You can reach Cape Blanco by driving 5.5 miles along the Cape Blanco Road from US 101, just south of the town of Sixes or 4 miles north of Port Orford. The green-shaded areas on the map are the surface of the marine terrace.

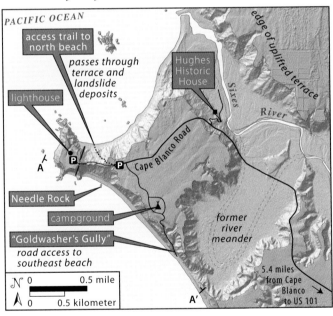

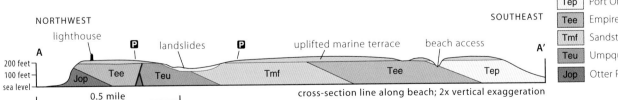

Tep	Port Orford Formation (Pleistocene)
Tee	Empire Formation (late Miocene)
Tmf	Sandstone of Floras Lake (Miocene)
Teu	Umpqua Group (Eocene)
Jop	Otter Point Formation (Jurassic)

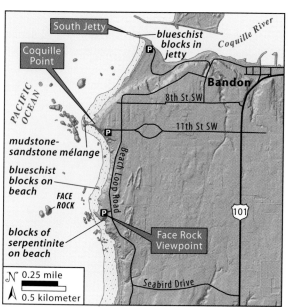

Bandon Beach, near the mouth of the Coquille River, is 25 miles south of Coos Bay and 27 miles north of Port Orford.

15 BANDON BEACH
Sea Stacks of Subduction Zone Mélange

Dotted by sea stacks, Bandon Beach is one of Oregon's best places to contemplate the Cascadia subduction zone some 50 miles to the west. Bandon's rocks came together in an earlier version of this subduction zone more than 100 million years ago. At low tide, you can walk far out on the beach and inspect many of the sea stacks, composed of a wide variety of rock that was formed mostly in Jurassic time, then mixed with other rocks in the Cretaceous subduction zone. While most of the sea stacks are highly fractured and faulted sandstone, many consist of other rock types, seemingly thrown together in a haphazard fashion. These rock types include red and green chert, blueschist, peridotite, and serpentinite, each characteristic of a completely different environment of formation. The chert formed at the bottom of a deep ocean, the blueschist from metamorphism in the subduction zone, the peridotite formed in Earth's mantle, and the serpentinite formed by metamorphism and alteration of the peridotite. Between these rocks are bodies of mudstone, much less resistant to erosion and so generally hidden beneath the sandy beach.

Looking north at the sea stacks of Bandon Beach. The flat top of the terrace on the right side of the photo projects westward to include the top of several sea stacks, most noticeably the large one near the center of the photo.

Main source and further reading: Baldwin and Beaulieu, 1973; Wiley and others, 2014

Geologists call this collection of disparate rock types a mélange, mixed together through the inexorable deformation caused by the sinking plate at a subduction zone. Some small-scale versions of mélange show up in the outcrops beneath Coquille Point. There, you can see scattered pieces of sandstone encased in a matrix of scaly mudstone, the sandstone mimicking the scattered large blocks and sea stacks along the beach.

Today, Bandon Beach shows abundant evidence for the uplift and erosion that so characterizes much of Oregon's coastline. The flat surface on top of the sea cliffs, as well as on many of the sea stacks offshore, marks a marine terrace, formed at sea level as a wave-cut bench similar to Sunset Bay (site 13) but then uplifted because of the convergence at the modern subduction zone. This terrace, called the Whiskey Run terrace, formed between 85,000 and 80,000 years ago and is a noticeably planar surface from Coos Bay to Cape Blanco. You can see some of the terrace deposits just below the parking lot at Face Rock Viewpoint.

Of course, with uplift comes erosional features like sea stacks, sea caves, sea cliffs, and arches—the visually appealing aspects of Bandon Beach in various stages of destruction. You can explore some small sea caves below the Face Rock Viewpoint, and watch waves crash through a small arch offshore near Coquille Point. Many of the coastal cliffs are rapidly giving way to landslides, and the sea stacks, which mark former positions of the shoreline, seem to be just about everywhere. Face Rock, perhaps the best known of the sea stacks, sits a quarter mile offshore, while other sea stacks sit even farther out, including Wash Rock, almost exactly 1 mile from Coquille Point.

Exposure of small-scale mélange in an outcrop below Coquille Point. The small light-colored blocks of sandstone within the scaly, dark shale are analogous to the sea stacks—much larger blocks of mélange.

A block of blueschist that weathered out of the nearby cliffs.

Blocks of red chert at low tide.

41

Sea arch eroded in the Otter Point Formation at Indian Sands.

16 INDIAN SANDS
Pleistocene Sand Dunes above a Sea Arch

Indian Sands presents one of the most dramatic and walk-able parts of Samuel Boardman State Scenic Corridor, a 12-mile stretch of some of Oregon's most rugged coastline, just north of Brookings. At Indian Sands, you can walk onto the colorful remains of Pleistocene sand dunes, inspect the sedimentary bedrock below the deposits, and view a dramatic sea arch. Active between about 40,000 to some 8,000 years ago, the dunes are now perched about 100 feet above the waves. They have yielded 12,000-year-old human artifacts, to establish the dunes as one of the oldest known archeological sites on the Oregon Coast.

The dune deposits are noticeably flat, but they rest on a highly irregular surface of knobs and depressions in the older bedrock, an expression of the land surface when the sand was first deposited. Within the deposits themselves, you can see traces of inclined sand layers known as cross beds. Characteristic of sand dunes, cross beds form as windblown sand continually gets deposited in layers on the steep downwind side of migrating dunes.

The deposits at Indian Sands erode easily, and as they do, they release their sand, which gets further sorted into grains of similar size and redeposited by the wind as small

Main sources and further reading: Davis, 2006; Dott, 1971; Peterson and others, 2007

modern dunes. If you look at the sand with a magnifying glass, you can see that it's amazingly colorful, with mostly clear rounded quartz grains, black magnetite, and variably colored tiny rock fragments.

The bedrock beneath the dune deposits consists of sandstone and conglomerate of the Otter Point Formation, deposited in a deep ocean during the Jurassic Period. Individual layers are steeply inclined and appear to run into the sea, so that erosion of the softer beds creates narrow chasms now filled with churning waves. As you make your way southward along the edge of the sea cliffs, the rocks bend somewhat so that they tilt down into the water. There, erosion of the softer beds carved a sea arch.

Notice how the orangish Pleistocene sand deposits are eroding into modern dunes. The bedrock in the foreground is at a higher elevation than much of the windblown sand, which illustrates the irregular nature of the surface on which the sand was deposited.

Conglomerate of the Otter Point Formation. In the background, you can see the overlying Pleistocene sand.

To reach Indian Sands Trail, head north about 8 miles on US 101 from Brookings.

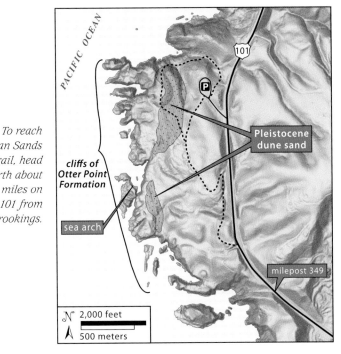

43

17 RAINBOW ROCK
Folded and Faulted Ribbon Chert

Rainbow Rock, one of Oregon's most colorful headlands, is composed of layered red, green, and white chert. It's surrounded on all sides by other rock to form a large isolated block in mélange of the Franciscan Complex of Jurassic age. You can view Rainbow Rock from the north end of a large pullout at milepost 354 on US 101, about 4 miles north of Brookings, and you can see it close-up by walking the beach at low tide, accessed by a narrow trail at the south end of the pullout.

The chert at Rainbow Rock formed through the accumulation of countless radiolarians, single-celled creatures that float in the ocean and produce tiny skeletons of silica, typically smaller than one-fifth of a millimeter. When radiolarians die, they settle to the seafloor to form a silica-rich ooze that can turn into chert. Frequently called ribbon chert because of their consistent thin-bedded nature, they are typical of deep-ocean environments where other materials tend not to accumulate. Trace amounts of oxidized iron colors the chert red, whereas reduced iron may color it green.

From the beach, you can see the intensity and variation of folding and faulting in the rock. Similar to pages sliding against each other when you fold a thick paperback book, ribbon chert folds easily because the thin layers can easily slide relative to one another. The rock is also highly broken by small faults and quartz-filled fractures. Many of the faults cut right across the bedding and are easy to spot, but others seem to vanish into the bedding itself. During low tides at Rainbow Rock, you can explore a sea cave and walk up to some small sea stacks, two of which are composed of the same chert as the headland.

Entrance to the small sea cave in the folded chert of Rainbow Rock. The cave continues some 50 feet to open to the front of the headland.

Main source and further reading: Dott, 1971

Geologists and folded and faulted ribbon chert.

Folded ribbon chert and sea stacks of Rainbow Rock at high tide as seen from US 101.

18 OREGON CAVES NATIONAL MONUMENT
Folded Marble Inside and Out

A spring gushes from the cave entrance at Oregon Caves National Monument. Inside the cave, it flows freely as an underground stream. Unlike the lava tube caves throughout most of Oregon that formed during the flow of lava, Oregon Caves formed by dissolution of marble bedrock, which originated as limestone in an ocean reef during the Triassic Period. It's part of the Rattlesnake Creek terrane, an island arc complex that was accreted to North America near the end of Jurassic time. During the accretion, the limestone was buried, metamorphosed to marble, and became highly deformed. Along the way, it broke into a large fragment that became surrounded by other metamorphosed rocks that, being insoluble, form the outer limits of the cave system. There are 3 miles of passageways, a little over a half mile of which are accessed by the National Park Service tour.

As you walk from the parking lot to the visitor center and cave entrance, you can inspect mostly gray, highly folded marble outcrops along the road. Look for stringy white layers of chert that have been broken and pulled apart. You can see more marble outcrops along with views of the Illinois River valley by hiking the 1-mile-long Cliff Nature Trail. The 3.3-mile-long Big Tree Trail offers the chance to see metamorphosed sedimentary and volcanic rocks that surround the marble, but only as loose pieces along the forest trail. Other rocks include peridotite, found at the

Recently precipitated cave formation called Angel Falls formed along the right margin of a diorite dike in the Ghost Room. Note the layers in the marble to the right of Angel Falls.

Geologic map of Oregon Caves National Monument with park trails.

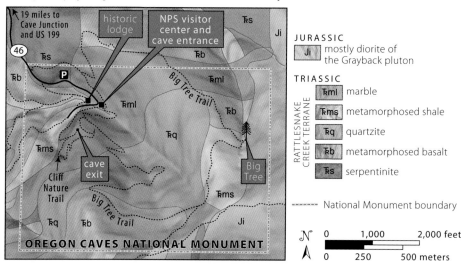

JURASSIC
Ji — mostly diorite of the Grayback pluton

TRIASSIC

RATTLESNAKE CREEK TERRANE

Ťml — marble
Ťms — metamorphosed shale
Ťq — quartzite
Ťb — metamorphosed basalt
Ťs — serpentinite

- - - - - National Monument boundary

0   1,000   2,000 feet
0   250   500 meters

Main sources and further reading: Covington, 2004; Kendall and others, 2011; National Park Service, 2011

Multiple stacked stalactites coat the walls of a vertical shaft in the Paradise Lost section of Oregon Caves.

outer parking lot, and diorite of the 160-million-year-old Grayback pluton, found along the park's eastern edge. The Grayback pluton intruded both the Rattlesnake Creek terrane and the adjoining Hayford terrane, telling us the terranes were already joined together before the magma intruded. You can find narrow dikes of the pluton in the marble just north of the Visitor Center along the Big Tree Trail and in the cave's Ghost Room.

The cave's mineral formations, called speleothems, include mostly flowstone and a variety of stalactites, stalagmites, cave "popcorn," and some columns. While the cave passages form through dissolution, the speleothems form by precipitation of calcium carbonate, typically drop by drop. Many of the smaller stalactites, called soda straws, grow down from the ceiling arranged in lines that define water-bearing cracks in the rock. Flowstone, sheets of calcium carbonate covering the marble, is deposited by a more dispersed flow of water over an even surface.

Wind and water brought sediment into the cave for at least 120,000 years. These sediments contain a rich fossil assemblage of mostly rodents, lizards, skunks, and salamanders, but also include larger animals, such as a 50,000-year-old grizzly bear and a 38,600-year-old jaguar.

Deformed marble along the road to the visitor center. Dashed lines show the outline of two folds in the rock.

47

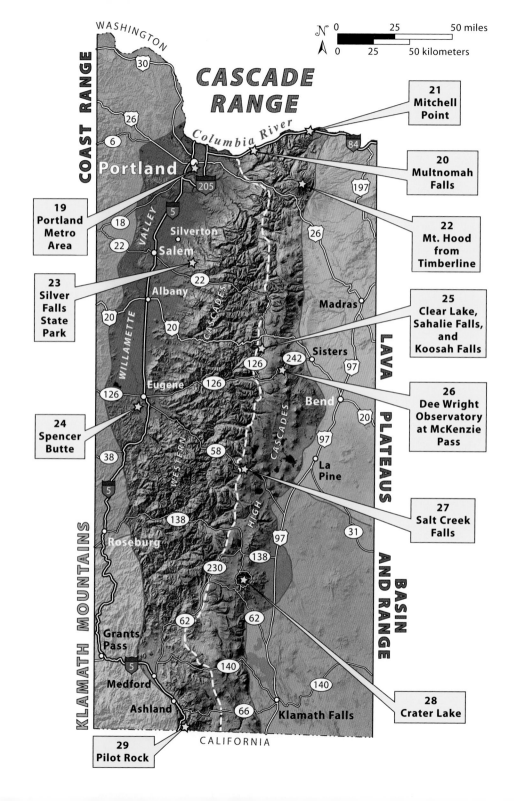

WASHINGTON

COAST RANGE

CASCADE RANGE

Columbia River

30

26

6

Portland

205

18

5

22

VALLEY

Silverton

Salem

22

Albany

CASCADES

20

20

WILLAMETTE

126

Eugene

126

58

WESTERN

38

5

138

Roseburg

KLAMATH MOUNTAINS

230

62

Grants
Pass

5

Medford

Ashland

66

CALIFORNIA

126

Madras

26

197

Sisters

242

97

Bend

97

20

La
Pine

HIGH CASCADES

97

138

62

31

Klamath Falls

140

140

LAVA PLATEAUS

BASIN AND RANGE

**21
Mitchell
Point**

**20
Multnomah
Falls**

**22
Mt. Hood
from
Timberline**

**25
Clear Lake,
Sahalie Falls,
and
Koosah Falls**

**26
Dee Wright
Observatory
at McKenzie
Pass**

**27
Salt Creek
Falls**

**28
Crater Lake**

**19
Portland
Metro
Area**

**23
Silver
Falls
State
Park**

**24
Spencer
Butte**

**29
Pilot Rock**

N 0   25   50 miles

0   25   50 kilometers

48

Aerial view at sunrise north over active volcanoes of the High Cascades from Mt. Bachelor in the center foreground to Mts. Hood, Adams, and Rainier in the background.

CASCADE RANGE

The Cascade Range forms a high spine up the western third of Oregon and extends northward through Washington to southern British Columbia and southward into northern California. In Oregon, the range consists of two parts, the Western Cascades and the High Cascades. The High Cascades mark the location of today's active volcanoes, from cinder cones and shield volcanoes to stratovolcanoes like Mt. Hood to the caldera of Crater Lake. The Western Cascades consist mostly of the lavas, ash-flow tuffs, lahars (volcanic mudflows), and igneous roots of long-extinct and deeply eroded volcanoes, much older but, overall, very similar to today's High Cascades. Both the Western and High Cascades formed because of subduction of the Juan de Fuca Plate beneath North America.

Although higher in elevation, the High Cascades show an overall gentler landscape than the Western Cascades. New lavas from the geologically frequent volcanic eruptions fill in many of the irregularities caused by erosion. The Western Cascades, being no longer active, show the effects of deep erosion: steep, deep river valleys and narrow ridgelines.

Between Portland and Hood River, the Columbia River cuts across the Cascade Range. As long as 16 million years ago, its valley provided a path for lavas of the Columbia River Basalt Group to course from eastern Oregon to the ocean. You can see those lavas in many places in the Columbia Gorge, including Multnomah Falls and Mitchell Point, as well as on the flanks of the Western Cascades at Silver Falls State Park east of Salem.

Rocky Butte   Mt. Tabor   Kelly Butte   Boring Hills   Mt. Scott

View of much of the Portland area looking east from the upper platform of the OHSU aerial tramway. On clear days, you can see Mt. Hood behind the Boring Hills, and Mt. St. Helens, north of the photo's view.

19 PORTLAND METRO AREA
Exciting Buttes of Boring Volcanics

Much of Portland's metropolitan area is dotted by buttes that rise between 300 and 900 feet above a landscape that otherwise slopes gently toward the Willamette or Columbia Rivers. Resistant to erosion, the buttes are composed of rocks of the Boring Volcanics and river deposits of the Troutdale Formation. Named for the town of Boring, just southeast of Portland, the Boring Volcanics erupted between 2.7 million and 56,000 years ago as basaltic lava flows, shield volcanoes, cinder cones, and even shallow intrusions. While we expect volcanic activity in the Cascades, these volcanoes erupted west of active volcanoes in the Cascades. This frequent and fairly recent volcanism in an urban area is unsettling, to say the least.

The Boring Volcanics erupted through and on top of the Troutdale Formation, which consists mostly of gravel deposited by an early rendition of the Columbia River between about 15 and 2 million years ago. The areas between the buttes were covered by up to 400 feet

of water during the Missoula Floods, which left behind deposits of gravel and sand.

You gain a wonderful view of the area from the top of the aerial tramway at the Oregon Health Sciences University. Uplift on the Portland Hills fault, which forms the front of the hills just west of downtown, creates the steep grade to the upper tram platform. At the aerial tramway, the fault lies east of the hills because erosion caused them to retreat. Reaching the tram terminal, at the corner of SW Bond Avenue and SW Whitaker Street in Portland, is easy by car, light rail, streetcar, or even bicycle—or you can forego the tram ride and access the upper tram terminal by foot, bicycle, or car.

At Mt. Tabor Park, you can see the western side of a small cinder cone that erupted about 200,000 years ago through the Troutdale Formation. Its eastern side was mined for use on park trails and walls. In cinder cones, the material ejected from the vent typically accumulates in

Main sources and further reading: Evarts and others, 2009; Ma and others, 2012

layers that tilt away from the vent, and here they all dip westward, away from the mined-out area, now a basketball court and amphitheater. A closer inspection of an exposure behind the amphitheater reveals some volcanic bombs among the broken rocks and cinders as well as small faults that likely formed during slumping. The exposure lies only a two-minute walk from the park visitor center.

At Joseph Wood Hill Park on Rocky Butte you gain fabulous views of the High Cascades, as well as much of the Boring volcanic field, including Mt. Tabor to the south, the Boring Hills to the southeast, and Larch Mountain, a high 1.5- to 1-million-year-old shield volcano directly to the east. Rocky Butte drops precipitously to the east, a consequence of erosion by the Missoula Floods, which burst from the Columbia Gorge to hit the butte head-on. On the north and west sides of the observation area, you can find some bedrock exposures of the basalt, which erupted about 285,000 years ago. You can also see scattered roadcuts on the way to the top.

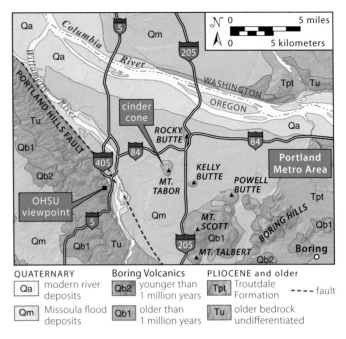

Geologic map of the Portland area. —Geology from Evarts and others, 2009; Ma and others, 2012

Exposure of a cinder cone behind the outdoor amphitheater at Mt. Tabor Park. Inset shows a lava bomb, identified by its elliptical shape, an interior filled with gas bubbles, and a rim that's practically devoid of gas bubbles.

Upper and Lower Multnomah Falls.

20 MULTNOMAH FALLS
Stacked Flows of Grande Ronde Basalt

At 620 feet, Multnomah Falls is the highest waterfall in Oregon. The creek plummets in two stages: an upper falls of 542 feet and a lower falls of 69 feet, with a 9-foot elevation change between them. The cliffs behind the falls consist of five separate lava flows of the Grande Ronde Basalt, which erupted in eastern Oregon between 16.0 and 15.6 million years ago and flowed down an older version of the Columbia River Gorge.

It's not easy to distinguish all the lava flows, but a few observations help. The topographic break that separates the upper and lower falls formed along a thin claystone layer that separates two flows, and near the top of the upper falls, you can see another flow, marked by pillow basalt that grades upward into a colonnade. Between these lower and upper flows lie three more. The lower two are separated by a fairly distinct but irregular contact. The second flow from the top lies just below the pillows and is only distinguishable because of its chemistry.

From the footbridge above the upper plunge pool, you can appreciate how waterfalls erode from their tops downward and from their bottoms upward. You can see a notch at the top of the falls where the water spills over the lip, causing enhanced erosion, and you can feel the power of the water as it hits the plunge pool, eroding an alcove deep into the bedrock behind the falls. As this alcove grows, the rock above it becomes unsupported and eventually falls, further enlarging the alcove and causing the cliff to retreat and maintain its near-vertical orientation. Indeed, a giant boulder, measuring some 40 feet by 20 feet by 6 feet, fell from the cliff in September 1995. It broke into several of the large boulders you can see around the bottom of the falls.

 Main sources and further reading: Beeson and Tolan, 1987; Reidel and others, 2013; Wells and others, 2009

There are two easy ways to get to Multnomah Falls, although given its popularity, parking can be a challenge. From I-84, you can take exit 31 for Multnomah Falls and park in the large lot between the east- and westbound lanes; from there, a short walk leads to the falls. You can also explore more of the Columbia Gorge and see several other waterfalls, some by trail, along the Historic Columbia River Highway by taking exit 28 if eastbound or exit 35 if westbound.

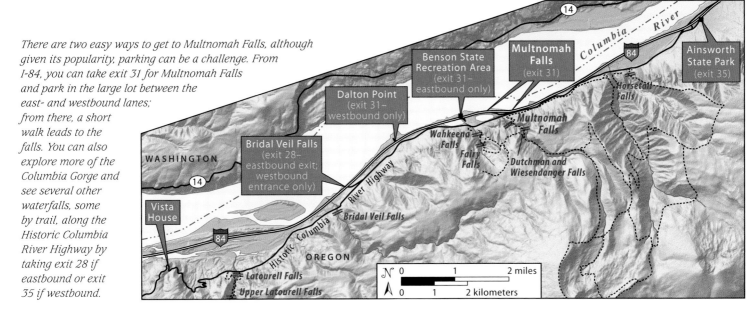

Close-up view at Multnomah Falls of the upper lava flow with pillow basalt (rounded blobs in upper third of photo) and lava flows beneath it, with columnar jointing.

Latourell Falls, along the Historic Columbia River Highway about 5 miles to the west, drops more than 200 feet over one of the youngest flows of the Grande Ronde Basalt. The columns form by shrinkage of the lava as it cools.

The lower cliffs at Mitchell Point consist of Grande Ronde Basalt, whereas the top of the upper cliffs is the Pomona Member of the Saddle Mountains Basalt. Below the Saddle Mountains Basalt lie river deposits (upper inset) of the ancient Columbia River, deposited against the side of a canyon carved into the Wanapum Basalt.

21 MITCHELL POINT
Ancient Gravel-Filled Columbia River Canyon

Cliffs of basalt drop practically into the Columbia River at Mitchell Point, where an unofficial rest area is available to eastbound travelers on I-84. The cliffs at the parking lot are part of the Grande Ronde Basalt, the most voluminous part of the Columbia River Basalt Group, erupted between 16 and 15.6 million years ago. Some 1,200 feet higher, more cliffs consist of the Pomona Member of the Saddle Mountains Basalt, erupted about 12 million years ago. Forming the base of the upper cliffs are thick deposits of gravel deposited by the Columbia River before eruption of the Pomona—indicating the Columbia River existed here before 12 million years ago. What's more, the gravel deposits appear to fill an ancient canyon carved into the Wanapum Basalt that lies between the Grande Ronde and

Saddle Mountains Basalt. Rivers cut down to form canyons when the land is uplifted, so the presence of a canyon, as opposed to a broad floodplain, likely marks an early period of uplift in the Cascades. With binoculars, you can see these deposits from the parking lot. You can also hike the trail to the top of the Mitchell Point, but be prepared for some difficult scrambling to reach the gravel deposits.

Also from the parking lot, notice the southward inclination of the rocks. They're on the south limb of an anticline that's part of the Yakima fold belt, which runs from near Portland to Lewiston, Idaho. From the viewpoint, you can see similarly inclined Grande Ronde Basalt forming the railroad tunnels across the river, although it's difficult to see because they're tilted directly toward you.

Main sources and further reading: Anderson, 1980; Tolan and Beeson, 1984

View up the Salmon River, about a quarter mile east on the Timberline Trail from the lodge area. The stream spills over bedrock of an approximately 135,000-year-old lava flow that's mostly covered by pyroclastic material from the Polallie and Timberline eruptive periods. The main summit area formed as a series of dome eruptions during the Polallie eruptive period 30,000 to 12,000 years ago; the crater area in front of the summit was exposed when the south side of the volcano failed during the Timberline eruptive period, depositing the apron of pyroclastic material that covers most of the area to the south; Crater Rock intruded during the Old Maid eruptive period between 1781 and 1800. Illumination Rock, on the far left side of the photo, consists of andesite that pre-dates the Polallie eruptive period.

22 MT. HOOD FROM TIMBERLINE
Oregon's Highest, Most Active, and Most Dangerous Volcano

Rising more than 2 miles above Portland, Mt. Hood's icy summit reaches an elevation of 11,250 feet, higher than any other point in Oregon. It's also Oregon's most recently active volcano, with a history of andesite and dacite eruptions that date back some 500,000 years. Its most recent history, which began 30,000 years ago and continues to modern times, occurred in three separate eruptive periods that built and shaped the modern volcano.

The results of each of these eruptive periods are in plain sight from Timberline Lodge, which is halfway up the volcano at 6,000 feet. The summit area and adjacent cliffs formed as a series of domes during the Polallie eruptive period, from 30,000 to 12,000 years ago; the cliffs show an array of colors from extensive hydrothermal alteration. From the parking area, you look up a broad apron of pyroclastic deposits that formed during the Timberline eruptive period between 1,700 and 1,400 years ago when the summit crater failed catastrophically to create its open, horseshoe shape. Most recently, from 1781 until about 1800, during the Old Maid eruptive period, a lava dome, called Crater Rock, intruded the crater.

As Crater Rock grew over a twenty-year interval, it repeatedly collapsed to produce dozens to hundreds of pyroclastic flows, many of which mixed with melting glacial ice to produce lahars. These deposits can be found on the south side of the volcano and down the Sandy River as far as the Columbia. Lewis and Clark, on passing the mouth of the Sandy River in 1805 and 1806, described a river that was choked with sediment, naming it Quicksand River.

Today, Mt. Hood is dormant, with scattered fumaroles, especially near Crater Rock. The area near the volcano also experiences one to two small earthquakes each month, but according the US Geological Survey, these earthquakes don't likely indicate volcanic activity. Monitoring stations on the mountain will alert scientists (and Portland residents, just 50 miles away) of impending eruptions. The Timberline area is a busy recreation destination, with numerous hiking trails and downhill skiing and snowboarding that typically continue through August. A paved road, just east of the town of Government Camp on US 26, leads 6 miles to Timberline Lodge.

Main sources and further reading: Cameron and Pringle, 1986; Hildreth, 2007; Scott and others, 1997; Scott and Gardner, 2017

23 SILVER FALLS STATE PARK
Alcoves behind Waterfalls

You don't just see waterfalls at Silver Falls State Park, you can walk behind several of them. A loop trail passes by ten of the park's fifteen falls, each of which spills over a lava flow of the Columbia River Basalt Group. Six of the falls drop more than 100 feet. The park owes its landscape to the nature of its bedrock and how it's been eroded by the North and South Forks of Silver Creek, which join near the northwest corner of the park. The basalt, being resistant to erosion, forms the steep-walled river gorges and waterfalls, whereas the more easily eroded Fern Ridge Tuff, which sits above the basalt, forms the surrounding hills. The tuff erupted explosively from a volcanic center in the Cascades between 11 and 7 million years ago.

The Grande Ronde Basalt occupies the lower elevations, with the overlying, younger Wanapum Basalt at higher elevations. Between them lies up to 20 feet of river-deposited sandstone and mudstone. These sedimentary rocks, which are easily eroded, contain molds of tree trunks and ancient soil horizons to suggest a forest became established between eruptions of the two basalts. The individual flows contain a range of features, beginning with a flow breccia near the base, a colonnade and entablature within the middle, and a zone with numerous gas bubbles near the top. In general, the colonnade, with deeply penetrating fractures that separate large columns of rock, erodes more quickly than the entablature, with its myriad small, discontinuous fractures.

Variations in the erodibility of the rock lead to the formation of alcoves behind the waterfalls, four of which are large enough to host a hiking trail. At North and South Falls, the alcoves are unusually deep, having formed along the sandstone and mudstone between the two basalts. At Lower South and Middle North Falls, the alcoves eroded within the colonnade, just below the overhanging and more resistant entablature.

Some of the greatest erosion takes place at the bottom of the falls, where the turbulent water scours out plunge pools. Over time, the rock above the pools, as well as the rock overhanging the alcoves, becomes destabilized and breaks off. In this way, the cliffs erode through time and the waterfall migrates upstream, often creating an amphitheater-like canyon.

At more than 9,000 acres and with nearly 45 miles of trail, Silver Falls is the largest state park in Oregon. It lies 28 miles east of downtown Salem.

Main sources and further reading: Freed, 1979; Reidel and others, 2013

The tallest waterfall in the state park, South Falls drops 177 feet. The water spills over a ledge of Wanapum Basalt and lands on Grande Ronde Basalt. The alcove behind the falls formed by erosion of the soft sedimentary rock between the two lavas.

A hiker on the trail behind Middle North Falls. The overhanging ledge at the top is the entablature, whereas the more-eroded part next to the trail consists of the colonnade with its vertical fractures.

Easily eroded sedimentary rock below just below the Wanapum Basalt at South Falls.

24 SPENCER BUTTE
Gabbro Intrusion of the Western Cascades

Rising 1,600 feet above the city of Eugene, Spencer Butte is composed of intrusive basaltic rock called gabbro that invaded the adjacent sedimentary rocks 32 million years ago. Because the gabbro is more resistant to weathering and erosion than the surrounding sandstone, it forms a prominent peak that provides a wonderful hiking area at the southern end of the Willamette Valley.

The gabbro of Spencer Butte belongs to a suite of similar intrusions that form many of the buttes lining the eastern edge of the Willamette Valley from Albany south to Creswell. These buttes include Peterson Butte near Lebanon and Skinner Butte on the north side of Eugene. Similar gabbro also forms flat, tabular-shaped intrusions called sills that hold up the hills just south of Eugene. The magma feeding these intrusions likely also fed many of the eruptions of the early Western Cascade volcanoes.

Eugene's ridgeline trail system accesses Spencer Butte's summit. You can also get there by a short trail from a parking lot high on Willamette Street. Along this shorter trail you can see a beautiful example of one of the many landslides that have sloughed off the sides of the butte. These landslides appear to localize near the boundary of the gabbro and the softer sandstone, and through time, they have made the top of the butte unusually steep. On clear days, the 360-degree view from the summit affords views of the Coast Range to the west, Willamette Valley to the north, the Cascade Range to the east, and the Camas Swale to the south.

Trails in Spencer Butte Park, on the south side of Eugene, can be accessed from several roads.

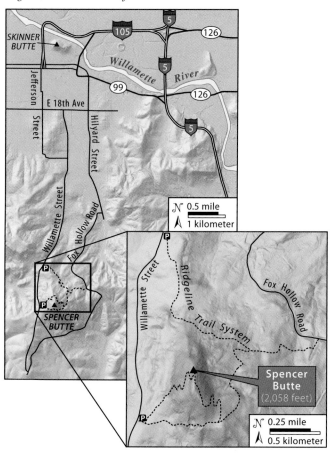

A close-up of the gabbro in which you can see individual mineral crystals.

Error

 Main source and further reading: McClaughry and others, 2010

Old landslide area and headscarp (steep slope behind trees) on the south side of Spencer Butte as seen from the trail. Numerous trees have grown in the landslide area since it formed.

View south over Eugene to Spencer Butte.

View southward from the summit of Spencer Butte toward the cloud-filled Camas Swale and the edge of the Western Cascades.

59

Upright Douglas-fir snag at the bottom of Clear Lake as seen from the boat dock.

25 CLEAR LAKE, SAHALIE FALLS, AND KOOSAH FALLS
Three McKenzie River Icons Formed by the Same Lava Flow

The McKenzie River begins at Clear Lake, and in just over 1 mile, spills over a basaltic lava flow to form Sahalie and Koosah Falls. The flow erupted from a nearby cinder cone about 3,000 years ago and dammed the existing valley. The lake backed up behind the lava dam, eventually over-flowing it.

The two waterfalls cascade over the same flow, not two flows like you might expect. How does a river drop over the same flow twice? It has to do with the geometry of the pre-lava valley. The base of the lava flow, which lies on top of the original valley floor, allows us to partially reconstruct the topography at the time of the eruption. It marks the bottom of Sahalie Falls, which sits at the same elevation as the bottom of Clear Lake, thus indicating this upper stretch of land was pretty flat prior to the eruption. Below Sahalie Falls, however, the base of the flow drops nearly 120 feet to the bottom of Koosah falls in only one-third mile, indicating a much steeper gradient. The lobe of lava flowed down this steep gradient, and now the McKenzie River flows down it, too, in the form of a second falls.

 Main sources and further reading: Cashman and others, 2009; Deligne and others, 2016; Deligne and others, 2017

The lava flow that dammed Clear Lake and formed the waterfalls came from the southern part of a series of cones called the Sand Lake volcanic field. The most visible of these vents is Little Nash Crater, at the intersection of US 20 with OR 22. These vents erupted basaltic flows and cinders all within the span of about one hundred years.

The unusual water clarity that gives Clear Lake its name derives from a lack of suspended sediment in the water as well as the water's unusually cold temperature. The lake gets its water primarily from springs, so there is very little input of sediment, and the spring water averages about 39 degrees Fahrenheit, cold enough to inhibit growth of algae that typically decreases the clarity of warmer lakes. The cold temperatures also preserved the trunks of Douglas-fir trees drowned by the rising waters behind the lava dam, some of which you can see from the boat dock, still in their standing positions. They and others toward the south end of the lake died when the lake backed up behind the lava flow at 3,000 years ago; trees near the northern end of the lake reside at a shallower depth and died a few decades later, probably during the eruption of the younger lava flow that forms much of the lake's eastern shore.

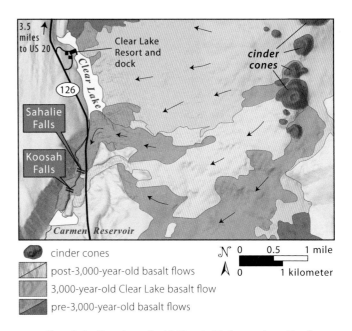

cinder cones

post-3,000-year-old basalt flows

3,000-year-old Clear Lake basalt flow

pre-3,000-year-old basalt flows

Clear Lake lies along the McKenzie Highway about 3 miles south of US 20.

Sahalie Falls, spilling over the side of the 3,000-year-old lava flow. Although nearly 1 mile away, the bottom of Clear Lake is at the same elevation as the base of the falls.

26 DEE WRIGHT OBSERVATORY AT MCKENZIE PASS
Cascade Volcanoes Rise above Young Lava

There's perhaps no better place in Oregon to see recent Cascade volcanism than the Dee Wright Observatory at McKenzie Pass. Here, a small rock shelter with an open-air viewing platform is surrounded by a 2,000-year-old basalt lava flow that erupted from Yapoah Crater, about 4 miles to the south but hidden from the field of view. Other flows near the pass, erupted between 3,000 and 1,500 years ago, came from Belknap and Little Belknap Craters just northwest of the observatory. These flows end near the Old Mckenzie Highway (OR 242) just west of the observatory. A paved half-mile interpretive trail starting on the east side of the observatory winds through the Yapoah lava and highlights several features typical of basaltic lava flows, including an open lava channel, pressure ridges, and large cooling fractures.

The short, steep walk to the viewing platform allows inspection of the 2,000-year-old lava. The flow consists mostly of the sharp, angular lava called aa, in contrast to the smoother, ropy-textured pahoehoe lava that you can see 1 mile down the road to the west on one of the Belknap flows. This difference is caused by the viscosity of the lava, with aa forming from the more viscous, less-fluid lava. Also, the rock is packed full of gas bubbles, called vesicles, as well as numerous small crystals of plagioclase.

A bronze plaque on the viewing platform identifies the surrounding peaks, nearly all of which are volcanoes. Only Mt. Jefferson, a stratovolcano due north of the observatory, is composed of andesite. Most of the other peaks consist of basalt or basaltic andesite, and many of them, including Mt. Jefferson, are built on large bases of basaltic flows. This preponderance of basalt and basaltic andesite typifies Oregon's High Cascades. Mt. Washington and North Sister, for example, are both deeply eroded basaltic andesite cones on top of large basaltic shields, while Middle Sister consists mostly of basalt. Belknap and Black Craters are both shield volcanoes, Black Crater having been deeply eroded by glaciers. Black Butte is a small stratovolcano of basaltic andesite.

View northward over the peak finder atop the viewing platform of the Dee Wright Observatory. The flow in the foreground erupted from Yapoah Crater. Mt. Washington and Mt. Jefferson form the spiky peaks in the background on the left and left-of-center, respectively. Black Butte forms the high rounded peak toward the right.

 Main sources and further reading: Cashman and others, 2009; Hildreth, 2007; Taylor, 1987

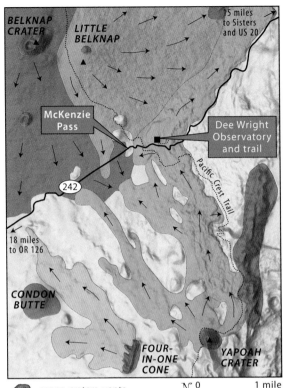

A lava channel, which concentrated flowing lava in its confines, as seen from the interpretive trail. Mt. Jefferson is in the background.

cones, craters, vents

Basalt Flows

Four-In-One flow ~2,000 years old

Yapoah flow ~2,000 years old

Little Belknap flow 1,500-1,300 years old

Belknap flow 1,500-1,300 years old

Geologic map showing most recent lava flows in the McKenzie Pass area. —Sources for the ages include Cascade Volcano Observatory (volcanoes.usgs.gov) and Deligne and others, 2017

The rock of the Yapoah flow is full of air bubbles (vesicles) and small white plagioclase crystals.

A section of the interpretive trail near its eastern limits passes through broken parts of a 30-foot-high lava levee that formed alongside the flowing lava.

27 SALT CREEK FALLS
High Cascades Lava in a Western Cascades Valley

With a drop of 286 feet over the edge of a thick flow of basaltic andesite, Salt Creek Falls is Oregon's second or third tallest waterfall, depending on how it's measured. Just over 5 miles west of Willamette Pass on OR 58 southeast of Eugene, the falls marks the place where young lava from the High Cascades meets the rugged landscape of the Western Cascades. Volcanism ceased some 8 to 4 million years ago in the Western Cascades, and erosion carved deep, steep-walled valleys. The lava flow that forms Salt Creek Falls erupted about 540,000 years ago from vents in the High Cascades and poured down a valley eroded into the old volcanic rock of the Western Cascades. Subsequent erosion reexcavated much of the valley to what it is today, leaving part of the lava flow as a 4-mile-long ridge that forms the modern valley's southern wall. You can see how the ancient valley was as deep as today's by looking at the rocks on the surrounding peaks. These 17- to 12-million-year-old volcanics rise more than 2,000 feet above the lava flow that forms the falls!

Salt Creek Falls from the upper overlook. It spills over a High Cascades lava flow and down a canyon floored by older volcanic rocks of the Western Cascades.

Main source and further reading: Sherrod, 1991

The most dramatic expression of today's erosion is the large alcove that partially encloses the plunge pool at the base of the falls. It's continually enlarging through the intense power of the falling water as well as the incessant mist that keeps the rock surface perpetually wet. During winter months, the water can freeze in the cracks, leading to enlargement of cracks. The waterfall retreats upriver because the presence of the alcove destabilizes the rocks above it.

The upper viewpoint, a short stroll from the parking area, gives a dizzying view of the falls as well as the chance to see cooling fractures in the lava in both cross-sectional and plan view. The short hike to the lower viewpoint lets you see fanning columns in the lava flow, produced by irregular cooling, and feel the heavy mist of the water as it sprays out from its plunge pool. Another trail leads southward to Diamond Creek Falls, which spills over the top of the same lava flow as Salt Creek Falls, but at an elevation 200 feet higher. The lava flow poured down into the ancient valley, so it drops in elevation along its path.

Close-up view of the basaltic andesite of Salt Creek Falls. It is very fine grained except for larger, partially weathered, glassy crystals of olivine, an iron and magnesium silicate mineral. Photo is about 1 centimeter across.

Cooling fractures in the lava flow as seen on its upper surface.

see glacial striations, scratches from rocks embedded in ice, on many outcrops on Mazama's flanks.

The caldera walls tell of Mazama's earlier history. They consist mostly of andesite lava flows that date back to 400,000 years. Phantom Ship, the little island at the southeastern edge of the caldera, consists of a 400,000-year-old andesite flow. Some important exceptions to the andesite include Mt. Scott, which formed on Mazama's flanks 420,000 years ago. It's composed of dacite, a rock intermediate in composition between andesite and rhyolite. The lava flow that makes up the Watchman is also dacite, but with an age of 50,000 years. Llao Rock, northeast of the Watchman, formed from a rhyolite flow that erupted on Mazama only a couple hundred years before the caldera-forming eruption.

As a general rule, lava flows indicate nonexplosive eruptions, while pyroclastic rocks, like pumice and ash flows, indicate explosive activity. Aside from the widespread pumice and thick ash-flow deposits from the caldera-forming eruption, the caldera walls contain very little pyroclastic rock. The lack of it might be a product of erosion instead of a lack of explosive behavior because pyroclastic rock is typically much easier to erode. Pumice Castle, the orange cliffs a little more than halfway up the caldera walls left of Mt. Scott (when viewed from the Watchman) is the most significant pyroclastic deposit. It consists of about 250 feet of pumice that erupted about 72,000 years ago.

CLEETWOOD LAVA FLOW

The Cleetwood lava flow, erupted during the earliest phases of the Mt. Mazama eruption, is exposed on both sides of Rim Drive near the trail to Cleetwood Cove. The lava and pumice fall and ash-flow deposits above it indicate that the caldera-forming eruption progressed rapidly, from extrusion of lava to wholesale failure of the volcano. The

The Cleetwood flow with overlying pumice deposited during the cataclysmic eruption. The pumice is highly welded where it directly overlies the rhyolitic rock, indicating the flow was still hot when it was deposited.

Cleetwood flow is a glassy rhyolitic lava flow and displays banding that formed parallel to its flow. On the lake side of the road, the banding is nearly vertical, whereas on the other side of the road, it's nearly horizontal. Charles Bacon, the US Geological Survey geologist who mapped Crater Lake in detail, showed how this lava oozed back into the caldera, forming the vertical banding. This pre-caldera lava was still hot enough to flow when the eruption proceeded and the caldera formed.

The overlying pumice fall deposit, which you can inspect on the north side of the road, marks the early explosive phases of the eruption. The pumice becomes increasingly dense and red toward its contact with the lava flow, another indication that the Cleetwood lava was still hot during the early explosive phases. Above the pumice, you can see light-colored ash and rock material enclosing several large blocks, broken rocks expelled when the eruption shifted into high gear.

THE PINNACLES

Some 6 miles down the glaciated Kerr Valley and into the Sand Creek valley, a series of narrow spires, called the Pinnacles, are eroded into Mazama's widespread ash-flow tuff. The deposit is about 150 feet thick and consists of rock fragments broken from the original volcano and enclosed in ash. You can see similar deposits along Annie Creek just outside the national park boundary.

The tuff eroded into narrow spires because of differential erosion, the spires being more resistant to erosion than the rest of the tuff. They formed as pipes, funneling gases upward from the base to the top of the flow. The gases, which likely originated because the ash flowed over a wetland area, precipitated minerals that cemented the soft material within the pipes into an unusually strong material. When Sand Creek reestablished its valley in the soft ash, the pipes were left standing as tall spires.

The Pinnacles were formed by differential erosion of gas-escape structures in the ash-flow tuff that erupted during the cataclysmic eruption.

The west side of Pilot Rock as seen from the trail. The present orientations of the cooling fractures near the summit, which likely formed vertically, suggest they've been tilted about 20 degrees eastward.

PILOT ROCK
A Siskiyou Landmark

Aptly named Tan-ts'atseniphtha, which means "rock standing up," by the Takelma Indians who inhabited the Rogue Valley, Pilot Rock rises some 570 feet out of the ground. With a base lying high in the Siskiyou Mountains along the California border, this highly visible landmark tops out at 5,910 feet, high enough to guide pioneers on the Applegate Trail. Pilot Rock is composed of dark-gray andesite and displays some stunning examples of columnar jointing, formed by contraction as the rock cooled. Once thought to be the eroded remnants of a lava flow, the rock is now viewed as a body of magma that cooled and crystallized beneath the surface, probably within the throat of a volcano. Researchers from Southern Oregon University dated the andesite at 25.6 million years, just a little younger than the surrounding rock. They also observed dikes that radiate out from Pilot Rock, especially on its eastern and western sides, filling fractures that likely formed during growth of the volcano.

To get to Pilot Rock, follow Old Highway 99 (OR 273) from the Mt. Ashland exit on I-5 (exit 6) south for about 2 miles to Pilot Rock Road. Turn left and follow the well-graded gravel road for another 2 miles to the parking lot. An interpretive display includes a map, and a clearly marked trail heads just over 1.5 miles (one way) to Pilot Rock's base, where you can see some of its spectacular columns. Most geologists suspect the columns formed vertically, in which case their present inclinations suggest they've been tilted some 20 degrees eastward, similar to the tilted bedding in rocks exposed elsewhere in the Siskiyous. Up close, you can see large black hornblende crystals in the rock that formed during its crystallization, as well as white zeolite minerals that fill gas bubbles in the rock. A difficult scramble from the base leads to the summit and a wonderful 360-degree view.

The Roxy Formation, which surrounds Pilot Rock, consists mostly of easily eroded lavas, tuffs, and lahars that

Main source and further reading: Knauss and others, 2008

Aerial view of Pilot Rock as seen from its east side. A dike forms the narrow rib of rock that descends through the trees directly below the cliffs. Inset shows a black amphibole (hornblende) crystal in the andesite of Pilot Rock. The white crystals are zeolites, minerals that filled cavities in the rock. Hand lens for scale.

Cooling fractures at the base of the summit scramble, which follows the crack where the two cliffs intersect.

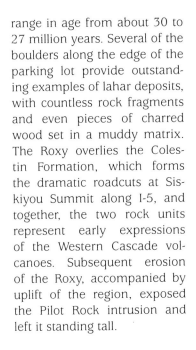

range in age from about 30 to 27 million years. Several of the boulders along the edge of the parking lot provide outstanding examples of lahar deposits, with countless rock fragments and even pieces of charred wood set in a muddy matrix. The Roxy overlies the Colestin Formation, which forms the dramatic roadcuts at Siskiyou Summit along I-5, and together, the two rock units represent early expressions of the Western Cascade volcanoes. Subsequent erosion of the Roxy, accompanied by uplift of the region, exposed the Pilot Rock intrusion and left it standing tall.

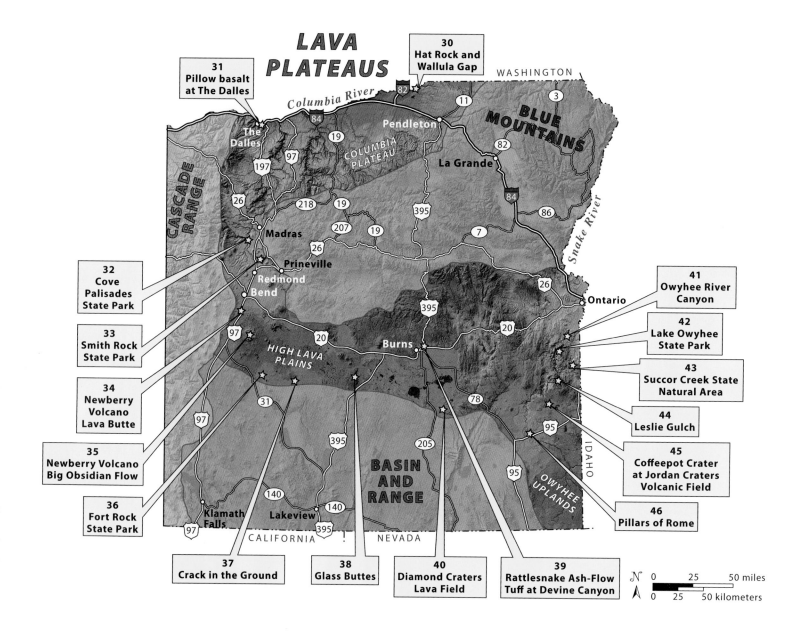

LAVA PLATEAUS

30
Hat Rock and Wallula Gap

31
Pillow basalt at The Dalles

WASHINGTON

Columbia River

Pendleton

BLUE MOUNTAINS

COLUMBIA PLATEAU

La Grande

CASCADE RANGE

The Dalles

Madras

Prineville

Redmond
Bend

Snake River

Ontario

32
Cove Palisades State Park

33
Smith Rock State Park

34
Newberry Volcano Lava Butte

35
Newberry Volcano Big Obsidian Flow

36
Fort Rock State Park

HIGH LAVA PLAINS

Burns

BASIN AND RANGE

OWYHEE UPLANDS

Klamath Falls

Lakeview

IDAHO

41
Owyhee River Canyon

42
Lake Owyhee State Park

43
Succor Creek State Natural Area

44
Leslie Gulch

45
Coffeepot Crater at Jordan Craters Volcanic Field

46
Pillars of Rome

CALIFORNIA

NEVADA

37
Crack in the Ground

38
Glass Buttes

40
Diamond Craters Lava Field

39
Rattlesnake Ash-Flow Tuff at Devine Canyon

0   25   50 miles
0   25   50 kilometers

Smith Rock and the Crooked River from the top of the Misery Ridge Trail in Smith Rock State Park, looking southwestward across the flat plateau toward the Three Sisters volcanoes. Basalt from Newberry Volcano floors the mesa on the far left side of the photo.

LAVA PLATEAUS

Oregon's lava plateaus, fairly low-relief surfaces compared to the rest of the state, form a broad horseshoe around the Blue Mountains. The plateaus are typically volcanic rocks, incised in places by deep river canyons. North of the Blue Mountains, these surfaces are part of the Columbia Plateau and consist largely of benches formed on lava flows of the Columbia River Basalt Group. South of the Blue Mountains in a region called the High Lava Plains and also in the Owyhee Upland, the bedrock is more variable. Vast open spaces developed on lava flows are punctuated in places by rhyolite eruptive centers such as Glass Buttes and the caldera at Newberry. Near the southern margin, the plateaus merge with the Basin and Range, so the landscape gets broken by numerous faults.

The Lava Plateaus produced several of Oregon's largest volcanic eruptions. Smith Rock is a product of a catastrophic eruption that formed the Crooked River caldera 29.5 million years ago. This caldera, barely discernable in the landscape today, stretched more than 20 miles from Smith Rock State Park to Prineville. Around 7 million years ago, a giant eruption near Burns formed the Rattlesnake Ash-Flow Tuff, which covered more than 10 percent of the state.

The Lava Plateaus also host some of Oregon's most recent volcanic eruptions. In fact, the 1,300-year-old Big Obsidian Flow at Newberry Volcano is Oregon's youngest lava flow, and numerous basaltic lavas at Newberry erupted between 7,100 and 7,000 years ago. Diamond Craters near Burns erupted about 7,500 years ago, while Jordan Craters near the Idaho border is even younger, at about 3,200 years.

30 HAT ROCK STATE PARK BELOW WALLULA GAP
Scablands Scoured by Missoula Floods

Hat Rock looks like a hat—at least according to the journal of Captain William Clark of the Lewis and Clark Expedition. They passed this Columbia River landmark October 19, 1805, soon after navigating a rapid. Today, Hat Rock forms the centerpiece of Hat Rock State Park and overlooks Lake Wallula, the reservoir behind McNary Dam. Upstream, the reservoir reaches into Washington through Wallula Gap, a 1-mile-wide canyon framed by cliffs of Wanapum and Saddle Mountains Basalts. Today's tranquility belies its origin as one of the more significant locations in the ravaged path of the Missoula Floods.

Between about 18,000 and 15,000 years ago, a lobe of the Cordilleran ice sheet blocked the Clark Fork River and impounded Glacial Lake Missoula, flooding thousands of square miles of the Clark Fork watershed in Montana to depths greater than 1,000 feet. When the lake broke through the dam, it released a flood that scoured much of northern Idaho and northeastern Washington. Once the lake emptied, the ice re-advanced across the river to block it again and repeat the sequence. Most geologists accept that there were at least forty of these gigantic floods over a period of 2,000 to 3,000 years. The first floods were the largest, with flows exceeding one hundred times the average discharge of the Mississippi River.

The 1-mile-wide Wallula Gap formed a constriction in the floods' flow path, causing the floodwater to back up into a temporary water body, named Lewis Lake for Meriwether Lewis. This lake extended across southern Washington almost as far east as Yakima and northward beyond Moses Lake and likely reached depths approaching 800 feet near the Tri-Cities of Pasco, Richland, and Kennewick.

Even though the larger floods overtopped the surrounding cliffs, Wallula Gap acted like a nozzle on a firehose. Estimates for water velocities and discharge through the gap reach 50 miles per hour and 400 million cubic feet per second. This action tore up the topsoil and much of the underlying bedrock to create scablands, which formed many of the rapids reported by Clark in his journals. These scablands now lie mostly hidden beneath Lake Wallula. Hat Rock, perched on the side of the river, is part of these scablands, a block of Wanapum Basalt that remains after everything else nearby was stripped away. A short hiking trail leads to the base of the rock.

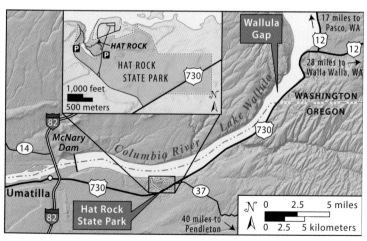

Hat Rock State Park received a direct blow from the Missoula floods as they funneled through Wallula Gap.

Close-up of cooling fractures in the basalt at Hat Rock.

Main source and further reading: Allen and others, 2009

Hat Rock and basalt outcrops. Boat Rock, another remnant of bedrock remaining after the ice age floods, forms the outcrop in the distance at center.

View up the Columbia River at Lake Wallula to Wallula Gap. The grain elevators mark the site of Port Kelley, Washington.

Outcrop of pillow basalt (dark, rounded blobs surrounded by tan matrix in lower half of photo) and a colonnade (vertically jointed cliffs in upper half) at The Dalles. Notice how the pillows slope southward (to the right).

Close-up of some basalt pillows and surrounding tan palagonite.

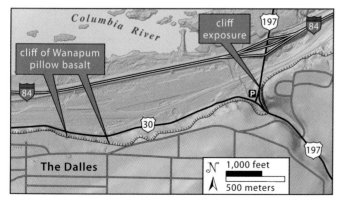

Much of The Dalles is built on the surface of the lava flow, which forms a large bench along the south side of the Columbia River.

31 PILLOW BASALT AT THE DALLES
A Lava Flow Filled a Lake

Many of the lava flows of the Columbia River Basalt Group encountered lakes as they flowed down the path of the Columbia River. Where the lava came into contact with cold water, individual blobs of lava formed rounded shapes called pillows. Abundant volcanic glass was also produced by the rapid cooling, forming glassy rims around the pillows. Most of the glass has since altered to the brown mineral palagonite.

You can inspect pillow basalts of the Wanapum Basalt across from a large pullout at the intersection of US 30 and US 197 in The Dalles. Many are highly broken by cooling fractures that run roughly perpendicular to their edges. Some of the pillows are nearly circular and entirely surrounded by palagonite, while others are elongate. The elongate pillows typically show an inclination southward, suggesting the original slope into the lake. The pillows grade upward into a beautiful colonnade with vertical columns of lava that cooled on land. As the first-arrived lavas filled the lake, the subsequent lavas flowed over land, on top of the pillows. You can trace the same flow for some distance to the east and west in The Dalles. It forms the large cliff-edged bench on which most of the city is situated, some 80 feet above the Columbia River.

Main sources and further reading: Reidel and others, 2013; Smith, 1998

32 COVE PALISADES STATE PARK
Basalt Flowed down One Canyon, Then up Another

The Deschutes and Crooked Rivers come together at Cove Palisades, where their deep canyon floors are submerged beneath the waters of Lake Billy Chinook, a reservoir. The canyon walls tell a story of an earlier canyon that was filled by basaltic lava flows that erupted 1.2 million years ago from a source about 60 miles to the south. On the geologic map you can see how this basalt (shown in orange) crops out in a narrow belt entirely within the confines of today's canyons. A lava flow such as this is known as an intracanyon basalt, and while the distribution of this intracanyon basalt alone suggests that it flowed down an existing canyon, at Cove Palisades you can actually see where it met the original canyon walls.

Probably the best place to see an edge of the original canyon is from the large pullout near the park's eastern entrance, at the top of the grade into today's Crooked River Canyon. The basalt flows, at road level to the south, butt up against the bedding in the older rock of the Deschutes Formation, which formed the walls of the old canyon. Since the eruption of the intracanyon basalt, the river reestablished its channel in the same place.

You can see another original canyon edge on the west side of the Deschutes River Canyon. Although it tells a similar story of lava filling the canyon, researchers have determined the lava flowed up, not down, the canyon! The basalt flowing down the Crooked River Canyon must have encountered an obstacle somewhere beyond that river's confluence with the Deschutes River, causing the lava to back up and flow part way up the Deschutes River Canyon.

Site continues on next page ———————➤

View northward up the Crooked River Arm of Lake Billy Chinook from the base of the Ship. The road grade down to lake level appears as a diagonal line beneath the canyon-rimming basalt in the background.

Main sources and further reading: Bishop and Smith, 1990; Bishop, 1990; Cashman and others, 2009; Smith, 1988, Taylor and Smith, 1987

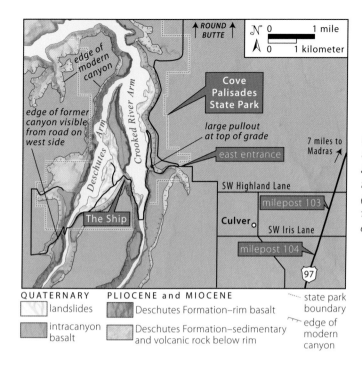

Geologic map of Cove Palisades State Park. The intracanyon basalt (orange) is entirely within the confines of today's canyon.

Map labels

edge of modern canyon

edge of former canyon visible from road on west side

ROUND BUTTE

N 0 — 1 mile
0 — 1 kilometer

Cove Palisades State Park

large pullout at top of grade

east entrance

7 miles to Madras

Deschutes Arm

Crooked River Arm

The Ship

SW Highland Lane

milepost 103

Culver

SW Iris Lane

milepost 104

97

Legend

QUATERNARY
- landslides
- intracanyon basalt

PLIOCENE and MIOCENE
- Deschutes Formation–rim basalt
- Deschutes Formation–sedimentary and volcanic rock below rim

.... state park boundary
🗲 edge of modern canyon

Billy Chinook Falls spills over the intracanyon basalt next to its contact with the Deschutes Formation (layered sediments at left), as seen from the pullout near the east entrance. Notice how the lava butts against a sloping valley wall in the older Deschutes Formation.

The Deschutes Formation consists of layered deposits erupted from High Cascade volcanoes between 7.5 and 4 million years ago. Altogether, the formation exceeds 2,000 feet in thickness. At Cove Palisades, the Deschutes Formation beautifully displays nearly its whole range of features, including preserved river channels, ash-fall deposits, sandy debris flows, welded ash-flow tuffs, and basaltic lava flows. Most of these features appear in the quarter-mile continuous exposure along the grade into the Crooked River Canyon. A prominent basaltic andesite flow, part of the Deschutes Formation, caps the softer volcanic sediments to form the rim of the modern canyon. It originated from Tetherow Butte, some 20 miles to the south, and also formed the rim of the older canyon. The Deschutes Formation includes the Ship, which displays a beautiful outcrop of welded tuff, and Round Butte, a small shield volcano 2 miles east-northeast of Round Butte Dam at the north end of Lake Billy Chinook.

The Ship—an exposure of the Deschutes Formation containing a prominent, thick, tan-colored welded tuff in its upper half.

Columnar jointing in the rim basalt, as seen from the top of the road grade.

79

Crooked River and cliffs of Smith Rock State Park. Smith Rock, composed of tuff, forms the monolith on the left side of the photo; a rhyolite dike forms the reddish tower on the right. Basalt of the Newberry Volcano caps the low mesa at left center.

33 SMITH ROCK STATE PARK
Edge of the Crooked River Caldera

The view from outside the small visitor center at Smith Rock State Park offers a landscape of contrasts. The parking lot and nearby camping and picnic areas are situated on the edge of a basaltic lava flow that drops off in a series of ledges to a narrow canyon that hosts the Crooked River, some 120 feet below. Across the canyon, tan cliffs and spires of tuff, a volcanic rock made mostly of consolidated ash and pumice, soar overhead. Smith Rock forms a peninsula of the tuff, enclosed by a hairpin bend of the Crooked River. The tuff erupted 29.5 million years ago in the largest volcanic eruption to occur entirely within Oregon.

The eruption created the gigantic Crooked River caldera, which stretches like an ellipse southeastward from Smith Rock more than 20 miles. Around its perimeter are rhyolite bodies that intruded after the eruption along ring fractures surrounding the caldera. The imposing red tower, just downstream from the hikers' bridge in Smith Rock State Park, is one of the rhyolite dikes that intruded after the eruption.

Some of the finer-grained, airborne material accumulated 75 miles to the east to form much of the blue- and green-colored Turtle Cove Member of the John Day Formation. All told, the eruption produced more than 140 cubic miles of material. The massive eruption as well as its caldera eluded detection until about 2006 when Jason McClaughry and Mark Ferns of the Oregon Department of Geology and Mineral Industries completed detailed mapping of the region. Now, some researchers even consider the eruption to be an early phase of the Yellowstone hot spot.

Text continues onto page 82————▶

 Main sources and further reading: McClaughry and others, 2009A; McClaughry and others, 2009B; Seligman and others, 2014; Smith, 1998

This cliff of tuff displays a prominent layering. Up close, the layering can be very subtle, as illustrated by the inset photo, which shows pumice grains. They are oriented parallel to the layering, but it's hard to tell in this close-up.

pumice

Geologic map of Smith Rock State Park at left. The tuff erupted from the Crooked River caldera (at right) and then was surrounded and partially covered by basalt from Newberry Volcano.

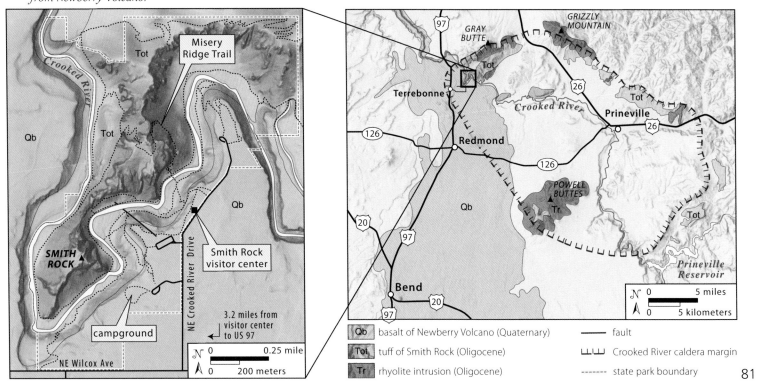

Crooked River

Tot

Misery Ridge Trail

Qb

Tot

SMITH ROCK

Smith Rock visitor center

NE Crooked River Drive

campground

NE Wilcox Ave

3.2 miles from visitor center to US 97

N 0   0.25 mile
   0   200 meters

97 GRAY BUTTE

GRIZZLY MOUNTAIN

Tot

Terrebonne

Crooked River

Prineville

26

126

Redmond

126

POWELL BUTTES

Tr

Qb

Tot

20

97

Bend

20

97

Prineville Reservoir

N 0   5 miles
   0   5 kilometers

Qb	basalt of Newberry Volcano (Quaternary)	———	fault
Tot	tuff of Smith Rock (Oligocene)	⊔⊔⊔	Crooked River caldera margin
Tr	rhyolite intrusion (Oligocene)	-------	state park boundary

81

Rock climber on the tuff of Smith Rock.

Cavernous weathering in the tuff. Note how the outer surface of the tuff is hardened by minerals, as seen at the bottom of the photo where it overhangs the easily eroded interior.

Hiking any of the park's numerous trails provides plenty of chances to see the tuff up close. Many tuffs become welded into hard rocks because of the high temperatures as they compact, but most of these tuffs are not welded. One exception is the red welded tuffs at the crest of the Misery Ridge Trail.

Some of the cliffs display a layering inclined roughly southward; up-close, it's typically defined by flattened pumice grains and subtle changes in the proportions of fine to coarse ash, a likely result of variations in the ferocity of the eruption. Many layers contain small rock fragments of older material incorporated into the eruption, including a tiny fraction of Permian-age limestone that came from the basement rock accreted during the Cretaceous Period.

Numerous pocket-like holes dot many of the cliff faces. The outer edges of these features typically consist of more durable rock, whereas the insides consist of softer, more easily erodible material. The durable crusts form because minerals in the rock dissolve in pore water and reprecipitate on the surface as the pore water evaporates, a process called case hardening. At Smith Rock, the responsible minerals are mostly zeolites, a group of minerals with wide-ranging compositions but containing silica, aluminum, and water. Along with the enhanced weathering and erosion along fractures, case hardening results in a wide variety of interesting shapes and pinnacles.

The basaltic lava flows at the state park originated from vents on the north side of Newberry Volcano some 400,000 years ago. They blanket the southwestern part of the Crooked River caldera and sit on top of the tuff in many places within the canyon. The lavas flowed around the tuff of Smith Rock on their way to the Deschutes Canyon, some 10 miles to the northwest. The highly irregular interface between the high-standing tuff and the basaltic lava was ripe for erosion by the Crooked River, which now meanders through a lovely gorge.

After the Lava Butte cinder cone formed, basaltic lava spilled out of the vent at its outer base to cover an area of about 9 square miles. The interpretive trail takes visitors right to the mouth of the vent (behind sign at bottom center).

 LAVA BUTTE AT NEWBERRY NATIONAL VOLCANIC MONUMENT
Iconic Cinder Cone at Oregon's Largest Volcano

Newberry Volcano forms a giant massif rising more than 3,500 feet above the nearby town of La Pine. With a volume exceeding 120 cubic miles and covering an area the size of Rhode Island, the volcano consists mostly of basaltic lava flows with a rhyolitic caldera at its summit. More than 400 volcanic vents, including cinder cones and fissures, dot Newberry's extensive surface. While Newberry's basaltic lava flows (some of its rhyolites) date back as far as 400,000 years ago, the rhyolitic caldera formed during an explosive eruption about 75,000 years ago, and much younger eruptions show the volcano is still active. Welded tuff from the caldera-forming eruption forms the cliffs behind Paulina Falls and covers much of Newberry's western slope. Lava River Cave, Oregon's longest known lava tube, formed in older lava flows.

Since the eruption of Mt. Mazama 7,700 years ago, Newberry has erupted both rhyolitic and basaltic lavas, including basaltic andesite. The rhyolites erupted within the caldera, and formed pumice deposits, pumice cones, and three obsidian flows. Big Obsidian Flow, the largest and youngest of these flows, erupted about 1,300 years ago and is described separately (site 35). The basaltic

Main sources and further reading: Cashman and others, 2009; Chitwood and others, 1977; Heath and others, 2015; Jensen and others, 2009; Jensen and Donnelly-Nolan, 2017; MacLeod and others, 1995; Smith, 1998

83

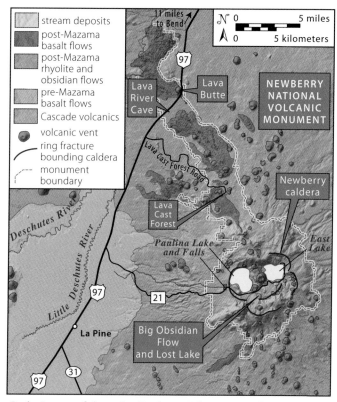

Geologic map of the active Newberry Volcano at Newberry Volcanic National Monument. Some flows erupted since Mt. Mazama blew its top 7,700 years ago.

Map legend:
- stream deposits
- post-Mazama basalt flows
- post-Mazama rhyolite and obsidian flows
- pre-Mazama basalt flows
- Cascade volcanics
- volcanic vent
- ring fracture bounding caldera
- monument boundary

11 miles to Bend

NEWBERRY NATIONAL VOLCANIC MONUMENT

Lava River Cave
Lava Butte
Lava Cast Forest Road
Newberry caldera
Lava Cast Forest
Paulina Lake and Falls
East Lake
Big Obsidian Flow and Lost Lake
Deschutes River
Little Deschutes River
La Pine

The interior of a volcanic bomb, a piece of molten lava that flew through the air and landed along the crater rim. The large air pockets form because of expanding gases in the core of the bomb.

lavas erupted along Newberry's northwest rift zone, which runs from the edge of the caldera to Lava Butte, some 13.5 miles away. The rift zone eruptions cluster in age around about 7,000 years ago. They produced thirteen separate lava flows, which include some beautifully preserved tree molds, where the lava flowed around a tree.

Based on the presence of hot springs and an unusually high geothermal gradient in the caldera, geologists have long suspected that a magma chamber may sit below Newberry caldera. In 2015, Ben Heath and his colleagues at the University of Oregon and University of Minnesota confirmed this hypothesis using seismology. They imaged a system between 2 to 3 miles deep that held at least 0.6 cubic miles of melt.

Rising more than 500 feet above the surrounding landscape, Lava Butte occupies the northern end of Newberry National Volcanic Monument. It hosts the Lava Lands Visitor Center, which offers numerous exhibits on the geology and ecology of the region as well as the trailhead for the Trail of the Molten Land loop. The visitor center marks the start of the short road that spirals to the top of the cinder cone. Like the other features in Newberry's northwest rift zone, Lava Butte formed between about 7,100 and 7,000 years ago. The eruption of Lava Butte also spawned a lava flow of basaltic andesite that covers an area of about 9 square miles and nearly encircles the butte.

Lava Butte's crater, which marks the central vent for the cone, reaches about 150 feet deep when measured from the butte's highest point. The rocks consist entirely of tephra—material ejected during

View over the crater of Lava Butte to Newberry Volcano in the distance and many of its cinder cones. Lavas erupted between 7,100 and 7,000 years ago occupy the less-vegetated areas in the middle ground.

the eruption and piled up around the vent, including ash, cinders, blocks, and bombs. Most of the tephra is red because of the high degree of oxidation of iron-containing minerals. In many places, you can see how the tephra welded together because of the high temperatures. Nearly all the rocks are full of gas bubbles, a reflection of the high gas content in the original magma and the explosive nature of the eruption.

By contrast, the lava flow reflects a far less explosive eruption. It spilled out of a vent on the south side of the butte and flowed mostly to the west and north for a distance of nearly 6 miles. The Trail of the Molten Land loops for 1.1 miles through parts of the lava flow, eventually reaching the vent at the bottom of the butte. The flow appears unusually fresh and devoid of trees for its age, as are other lavas of

the same age along the northwest rift. This slow weathering and lack of trees may have resulted from the lack of younger tephra deposits, which would break down quickly to nourish vegetation, even in the dry climate.

Lava Butte appears to show the same life cycle as many other cinder cones; the cone and subsequent lava flows form during different stages of a single eruption. In the early stages, the rising magma explodes from the vent because it contains high levels of dissolved water and gas, much like soda will burst from a shaken bottle. As the eruption proceeds, broken volcanic material accumulates around the vent and builds the cone. Eventually, the amount of gas and water decreases, so the explosiveness wanes to the point where the magma breaks through the side of the cone to form a lava flow.

35 BIG OBSIDIAN FLOW
A World of Glass at Newberry Volcano

About 1,300 years old, Big Obsidian Flow is Oregon's youngest lava flow. Its formation marked the final stage of an eruption that began explosively and covered the Newberry Volcano's caldera with up to 10 feet of pumice. The flow emerged from a vent near the southern edge of the caldera and flowed as a sticky mass more than 1 mile northward onto the caldera floor. Countless concentric pressure ridges decorate its surface, showing the path of the lava from its source, now a 200-feet-high dome.

Big Obsidian Flow is only about 10 percent obsidian, a volcanic glass. The rest is pumice. Air-filled and frothy to varying degrees, the pumice is also composed of glass and has exactly the same composition as the obsidian, just a remarkably different texture and color. The black color of obsidian derives from the presence of submicroscopic, dark crystals dispersed through the rock. The same minerals are also present in the light-colored pumice, but because of the rock's low density, they tend to be widely separated. Both obsidian and pumice are rhyolite, consisting of nearly 72 percent silica. They generally appear together as separate bands within the same rock. In many places, the banding shows folds and swirls that formed during flow of the hot glass. Variations in gas bubble size and strength, leading to overall differences in compactability as the lava flowed, provide the best explanation for the differences between pumice and obsidian in the rock.

Aerial view of Big Obsidian Flow, its surface lined with pressure ridges enhanced by snow. The ridges formed as the lava spread toward the north (bottom right). Behind the flow is the south wall of Newberry caldera. Cinder cones dot the landscape in the distance.

 Main sources and further reading: Jensen and others, 2009; Jensen and Donnelly-Nolan, 2017; MacLeod and others, 1995

Obsidian, which is easily worked into sharp tools, provided a valuable commodity for early inhabitants of the region and was traded widely throughout the Pacific Northwest. Material from Big Obsidian Flow was especially desirable because of the large sizes of so many of the obsidian blocks. However, the presence of worked obsidian in the caldera beneath ash from the Mazama eruption, dated at 7,700 years ago, indicates early peoples quarried the stone from the caldera's other obsidian flows *before* eruption of Big Obsidian Flow.

A short, steep hiking trail winds through the lower portions of the flow. Perhaps the most striking aspect of the hike is the lava flow's surface, which is broken and jagged. The multiple pressure ridges, easy to see from a distance, appear as irregular piles of broken rock along the trail. Close inspection of many of the rocks shows the interlayering of pumice and obsidian and the gradational nature between them. Lost Lake, fed by groundwater from beneath the flow, appears as the narrow lake in front of the flow's eastern lobe. Another trail follows the eastern edge of the flow all the way to the caldera rim, some 1,000 feet above.

Close-up view of obsidian, which shatters with conchoidal fractures typical of glass.

As the magma rose through its vent and flowed onto the land surface, the lava experienced a type of shear that caused its bubbles to squeeze together and compact. Some zones experienced more shear than others, and most compacted zones became obsidian (dark gray).

Black, solid obsidian interbedded with pumice. The broken rock of a pressure ridge forms the background.

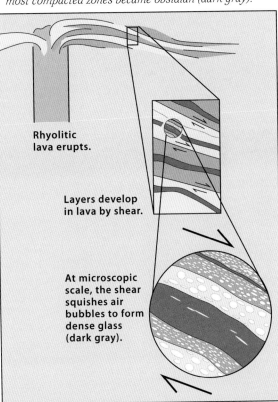

Rhyolitic lava erupts.

Layers develop in lava by shear.

At microscopic scale, the shear squishes air bubbles to form dense glass (dark gray).

87

Fort Rock rises more than 200 feet above sage-covered valley.

 36 **FORT ROCK STATE PARK**
Steam Eruption Forms Tuff Ring

With circling walls that rise more than 200 feet straight up from a nearly flat valley floor, Fort Rock *looks* like a fort. In reality it's a tuff ring, formed when basaltic lava erupted through a lake that filled the Fort Rock–Christmas Valley area, probably about 150,000 years ago during glacial times. The erupting lava flashed the lake water to steam, creating explosions that broke the lava into countless glass and rock fragments. The resulting tuff accumulated in layers around the vent because the eruption pulsated from different batches of lava contacting the lake water. Much of the glass, formed throughout the deposit by the abrupt cooling, further interacted with the water to change into a yellow-brown material called palagonite.

The lake water reached a depth of about 65 feet, based on the elevations of the two prominent benches that mark shorelines on the south side of Fort Rock. The waves easily eroded the outer margins of the deposit, which being farther from the vent and lacking the heat necessary to weld, accumulated as loose material. By contrast, materials closer to the vent welded together to form a more resistant rock and today stand up as cliffs. The southern wall of the ring was removed altogether by waves driven by the prevailing southerly winds. A prominent notch undercuts the cliff at the eastern shoreline bench as a testament to the wave action.

Close inspection of the rock reveals that it's a mixture of dark-gray fragments of basalt suspended in a yellowish-orange matrix of palagonite. Individual layers show differences in particle sizes or concentrations—and some even show gradations from coarser to finer grain sizes upward, typical of air-fall deposition. Perhaps most striking, however, is that many of the layers dip inward toward the crater, rather than outward, away from it. These beds

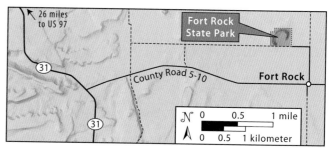

Fort Rock State Park is 40 miles southeast of La Pine off OR 31.

Main source and further reading: Brand and Heiken, 2009

Close-up view of the tuff and its bedding, oriented diagonally from upper left to lower right. It consists mostly of basalt fragments and orange-brown palagonite.

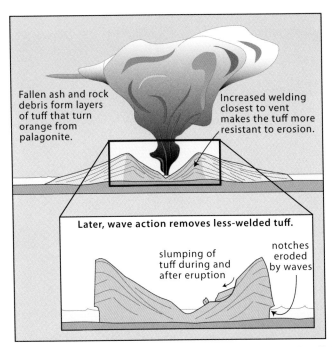

Fallen ash and rock debris form layers of tuff that turn orange from palagonite.

Increased welding closest to vent makes the tuff more resistant to erosion.

Later, wave action removes less-welded tuff.

slumping of tuff during and after eruption

notches eroded by waves

Pulsating eruptions through an ice age lake formed the Fort Rock tuff ring.

formed on the inside of ring; the less-welded outer side having eroded away.

Further complexities in the bedding orientations resulted from the presence of water during the eruption, as sections of the deposit frequently slumped into the lake. The park trail, which circles the interior of the ring, passes behind one of the larger slump blocks near the northwestern edge of the crater. Because deposition and slumping were taking place simultaneously during the eruption, newly deposited material formed at inconsistent or unusual angles. Some geologists suggest that the eruption waned as the water supply diminished, which caused the deposits higher in the cliffs to be finer grained and take on a duller shade of orange from having less palagonite, a change that's easily observed from within the crater.

Wave-cut notch and part of Fort Rock's interior. Note how the bedding is inclined steeply inward.

Narrow passage along the southern part of Crack in the Ground.

37 CRACK IN THE GROUND
Fault at Four Craters Lava Field

In the remote region of Christmas Valley, you can walk into a deep crack that formed over a normal fault. Aptly named Crack in the Ground, it extends in a northwesterly direction for about 4 miles, reaching depths of up to 70 feet. The crack formed within 740,000-year-old basalt from Green Mountain, a shield volcano. Movement on a fault deep beneath the surface caused the basalt to gently bend and break, and then pull apart. In some places the uplifted western side of Crack in the Ground is nearly 15 feet higher than the eastern side and in other places the walls are only a few feet apart.

Most researchers argue that Crack in the Ground formed at the same time as the adjacent Four Craters lava field, marked by a chain of four cinder cones that's roughly parallel to but about 1 mile northeast of the fault. They observe that the Four Craters lava, only 14,000 years old, flows into the crack along one section of its length and is elsewhere partially broken by the crack. In addition, by dating the age of the rock surfaces exposed in the crack, Ben Mackey and his colleagues at the University of Oregon found that it was 14,000 years old, plus or minus 1,000 years, the same age as the lava flow. Their observations show how volcanism and normal faulting, which is driven by extension of the crust, can be related.

You can access Crack in the Ground from two places along Crack in the Ground Road, which heads north from the town of Christmas Valley. At both places, you can see how the western wall tends to be higher than the eastern wall, and how both walls tend to fit back into place like a jigsaw puzzle. The elevation difference reflects uplift of the western block and folding of the basalt. The jigsaw-like fit reflects breakage and pulling away of the crack walls. At the northern access, you can see the Four Craters lava filling part of the crack. A little searching along the mostly buried trace of Crack in the Ground in this vicinity shows that the young lava is itself broken by the crack.

 Main source and further reading: Mackey and others, 2014, Pezzopane and Weldon, 1993

Aerial view of Crack in the Ground and the Four Craters lava field, looking north. Three of the four cinder cones are visible along the right side of the photo. Green Mountain shield volcano is visible in the distance on the left. Note how the young black lava covers the northern extent of the crack.

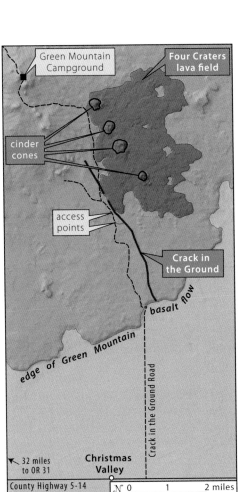

Geologic map of Crack in the Ground, a remote site about 7 miles north of the town of Christmas Valley.

Northern extent of the Crack in the Ground where it's filled by lava from the Four Craters.

91

38 GLASS BUTTES
Obsidian in Rhyolite Domes

True to the name, Glass Buttes offers many opportunities for collecting obsidian, a volcanic glass. You can even see countless small pieces of the volcanic glass littering the gravel access road. Glass Butte and Little Glass Butte, about 4 miles to the southeast, dominate this volcanic complex of more than a dozen isolated hills and ridges. They formed as a series of rhyolitic lava domes and flows that erupted in multiple events beginning 6.5 million years ago near the southeast part of the field and ending 4.9 million years ago with eruption of the high summit of Glass Butte.

At least three obsidian flows lie within the volcanic complex, mostly in the vicinity of Little Glass Butte. In their time, they likely resembled smaller versions of the Big Obsidian Flow at Newberry (site 35). Because obsidian flows are so broken and full of pumice, they weather and erode more quickly than the surrounding rhyolite flows and tend to be covered by soil and vegetation. Obsidian, though, is very resistant to weathering because of its impermeability. Collectors find most of the obsidian loose on the ground or mine it from the many prospect pits.

Obsidian comes in numerous colors, depending largely on the presence of submicroscopic, iron-rich crystals in the rock, which color it black, and their degree of oxidation, which provides color to varieties such as mahogany, rainbow, and flame obsidian. The white spots on snowflake obsidian, by contrast, form from radiating tiny crystals of silica that grow long after the rock cools. Glass Buttes hosts each of these varieties, and its obsidian has been highly prized and traded for a long time. Glass Buttes obsidian has been found in archeological sites ranging from northern California to British Columbia and as far east as Ohio.

Several northwest-trending faults of the Brothers fault zone, which forms a diffuse zone of faulting from near Bend to south of Burns, cut the buttes. Although they don't offset individual flows very far, the faults provided pathways for hydrothermal fluids to invade the adjacent fractured rock and deposit cinnabar, a highly toxic mercury sulfide. Mining of cinnabar took place from 1933 to the early 1960s on the northeast side of the complex.

Surrounding the buttes are basalt flows that erupted between about 6.5 and 1.4 million years ago. This contemporaneity of rhyolitic and basaltic eruptions is typical of the High Lava Plains. You can see many of the basalt flows, broken into ridges by the Brothers fault zone, along US 20.

Glass Butte, as viewed from the northwest on US 20. The low ridge near the bottom of the photo rises abruptly along a fault of the Brothers fault zone.

Main sources and further reading: Berri, 1982; Boschman, 2012; Johnson and Ciancanelli, 1984

Little Glass Butte.

Geologic map of the Glass Buttes area.
—Simplified from Berry, 1982 and Boschman, 2012

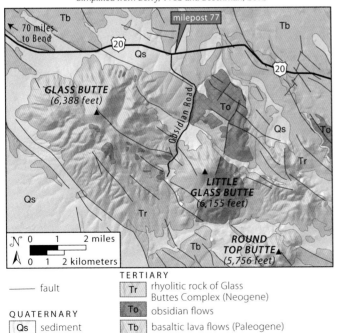

Black and mahogany obsidian can be found concentrated naturally on the surface.

Black obsidian found in one of the many prospecting pits in the area.

93

Roadside exposure of Rattlesnake Ash-Flow Tuff. The whitish ash-fall layers at its base sit on top of older, orangish sedimentary rock. The tuff measures 72 feet, the full thickness visible in this photo, and consists of several ash flows that all cooled together.

39 RATTLESNAKE ASH-FLOW TUFF AT DEVINE CANYON
A 7-Million-Year-Old Catastrophe

As you drive north just over 6 miles from Burns on US 395, you see the entrance to Devine Canyon appear as a notch in a low plateau, a subdued impression that belies one of Oregon's most destructive events. The plateau is capped by the Rattlesnake Ash-Flow Tuff, which formed in a catastrophic eruption 7 million years ago and incinerated more than 10 percent of Oregon's land surface in a matter of hours. Thick exposures of the tuff exist about 70 miles to the north at the Sheep Rock Unit of the John Day Fossil Beds National Monument (site 49) and some 65 miles to the south on Steens Mountain (site 57). Two older ash-flow tuffs, formed during major eruptions 10 and 8.5 million years ago, are also exposed in Devine Canyon.

At an obvious pullout just south of milepost 64, the Rattlesnake Ash-Flow Tuff forms an imposing outcrop that sits directly on top of a few feet of peach-colored, volcanic-rich sedimentary rock. The tuff consists of several successive ash flows that all cooled together, measuring some 72 feet in combined thickness. With just casual inspection, you can tell that it's zoned, beginning with a thinly layered, whitish ash-fall deposit at its base and finishing with a resistant brown cliff at its top. Geologists define eight separate zones, depending on the degree of welding, type of matrix material, and glass content. The upper part is full of mineral-filled gas pockets, called lithophysae, which form by minerals crystallizing from vapor during the last stages of cooling.

The rocks tilt gently southward in Divine Canyon, so if you drive northward up US 395, you'll encounter older tuffs at road level. Near milepost 63, you can see the 8.5-million-year-old Prater Creek Tuff, and at milepost 62, the 9.7-million-year-old Devine Canyon Tuff. The sources of these tuffs, although different from the Rattlesnake Ash-Flow Tuff, were also likely in the general vicinity of Burns.

Main sources and further reading: Jordan and others, 2002; Streck and Ferns, 2004

The 8.5-million-year-old Prater Creek Tuff is exposed along US 395, 1 mile north of the Rattlesnake Ash-Flow Tuff exposure. The Rattlesnake Ash-Flow Tuff caps the hill in the background.

The original caldera for the tuff was likely about 25 miles to the southwest of Burns, near the center of the tuff's regional distribution. There, the tuff contains the largest pumice blocks and shows the greatest degree of welding, which suggests it was hotter. —Jordan and others, 2002

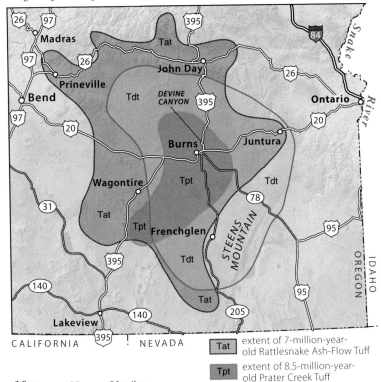

Tat	extent of 7-million-year-old Rattlesnake Ash-Flow Tuff
Tpt	extent of 8.5-million-year-old Prater Creek Tuff
Tdt	extent of 9.7-million-year-old Devine Canyon Tuff

N
0   25   50 miles
0   25   50 kilometers

Lithophysae, mineral-filled gas pockets, are found throughout much of the tuff in Devine Canyon.

95

Lava Pit Crater with South Dome in the background.

40 DIAMOND CRATERS LAVA FIELD
A Jewel of Domes and Maar Explosions

The Diamond Craters lava field, named for the nearby town of Diamond, offers an array of pit and explosion craters, collapsed domes, grassy fields of ejected cinder, and some fresh lava flows. They're all built on and around what's probably a small shield volcano that covers an area of 27 square miles. According to studies by David Sherrod and his colleagues at the US Geological Survey, the lava field formed between 7,790 and 7,320 years ago and erupted more than a third of a cubic mile of magma.

Perhaps the most striking thing about the lava field is its profile. Lava flows are usually pretty flat, but this lava field consists of four domes, each of which stretches more than 1 mile in length and reaches 200 to 500 feet high. The injection of younger lava beneath existing flows caused everything to arch upward, forming the domes. To complicate the matter, the central block of Graben Dome, on the east side of the complex, dropped downward during this stage along two faults that run the length of the dome.

Many of the features of Diamond Craters can be seen from roads. From Lava Beds Road, the paved road along its south end, you can see beautiful ropy pahoehoe lava in the young lava flows that issued from vents around the perimeter, called flank eruptions. In some places are miniature versions of the larger domes, called tumuli (singular: tumulus), where an existing flow became arched upward and cracked by inflation from new lava below.

You can see several of the craters from the well-maintained gravel road along the lava field's southwestern side. Some of them, most notably Lava Pit Crater, formed through collapse after removal of lava from the crater's vent. These collapsed craters are generally rimmed by lava bedrock. Other craters, including those in the central vent complex, are maars, formed when rising basaltic magma intersected groundwater. The resulting steam explosions from these maars formed craters more than 60 feet deep and ejected the cinders that now blanket the landscape.

 Main sources and further reading: Benedict, 1985; Chitwood, 1994; Peterson and Groh, 1964; Sherrod and others, 2012

These craters may or may not have bedrock exposed but tend to have sloping sides resembling a funnel.

The northwest edge of the central vent complex is only a quarter mile from the gravel road. It is shaped like a horseshoe, nearly 1 mile long and 0.5 mile wide, and contains more than thirty vents, mostly expressed as overlapping funnel-shaped maar craters. Surrounding the vents is a moat that appears to follow a fault zone, which allowed the complex to drop downward like a caldera after their eruptions.

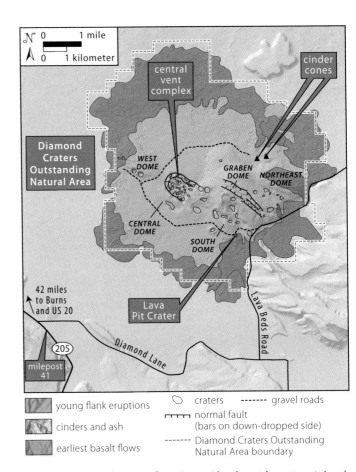

To reach Diamond Craters from Burns (the closest large town), head south on OR 205 for 52 miles, then turn east on Diamond Lane.

Tumulus, an arch in one of the recent flank lavas, formed by inflation from the influx of lava below—a small-scale analog to the doming at Diamond Craters.

View northward over the central vent complex.

97

View down-stream of the Owyhee River. The road passes gently dipping basalt flows and interbedded reddish tuffs and volcanic-rich sedimentary rocks.

 OWYHEE RIVER CANYON
Incised Meanders Expose Red Basalt and Flow-Banded Rhyolite

The Owyhee River rises in northern Nevada and flows 280 miles to the Snake River, traversing some of Nevada's and Oregon's most wild and remote landscapes. For 14 miles below Owyhee Dam, along the river's lower reaches, the Owyhee carved a narrow, winding canyon that is both easily accessible and spectacular. From the air, the bends in the canyon look like the meanders of a river flowing freely over a broad floodplain, not those of a river incised in an 800-foot-deep canyon. The deep, winding canyon of the Owyhee likely originated as meanders on a floodplain when the river was at a much higher level and cutting through softer sedimentary rocks. Then, regional uplift caused the meandering river to cut deeper into its channel to the point where it got trapped in harder rock.

The Owyhee Basalt, the main bedrock of the canyon, consists of more than a dozen individual flows of mostly medium-gray, finely crystalline basalt. Between the flows, beds of volcanic-rich sedimentary rocks, tuffs, and breccias lend extraordinary red colors to the canyon. The sequence measures more than 1,000 feet thick in places and formed between about 14 and 13 million years ago.

To see a cornucopia of interesting features on the road to the dam, head west on Owyhee Avenue from Owyhee, south of Nyssa. Set your odometer where you turn south on Owyhee Lake Road (see map on page 101). You enter the canyon at about 4.5 miles and by 4.7 miles encounter steam and a small hot spring that issue from a fault zone in the adjacent cliffs. A penstock that siphons irrigation

Main sources and further reading: Ferns and others, 1993a; Kittleman, 1973

Natural arch in red, layered volcanic rocks lies just downhill from of a grayish-brown basaltic dike that slopes down to the bottom left of the photo. Viewed at 13 miles down the canyon from the intersection of Owyhee Lake Road and Owyhee Avenue.

View from Owyhee Dam. Rocks in the foreground are rhyolite, stained by the reservoir high-water mark. In the background are stacked lava flows of the Owyhee.

99

Vertical flow-banding in rhyolite and obsidian in outcrop next to the dam overlook.

from Owyhee Reservoir crosses the canyon immediately upstream. At 6.3 miles, Snively Hot Spring issues from another fault, this one much less apparent. At 13.0 miles, look for a resistant basaltic dike just behind a natural arch on the cliff across the river. A half-mile farther upriver, you can see more dikes just before passing through a former railroad tunnel cut through red-stained Owyhee Basalt. At mile 18.1, the steep grade to the dam passes a basaltic dike intruding lahar (volcanic mudflow) deposits of the Succor Creek Formation, which lies just beneath the Owyhee Basalt.

At mile 18.4, you reach Owyhee Dam, which impounds Owyhee Reservoir. Completed in 1932, the dam is built into older rhyolitic lavas that here reach 1,000 feet in thickness but become thinner away from the dam site. Unlike the nearly horizontal basalts above, the rhyolites show a less-prominent, nearly vertical layering formed by upward flow of the magma. You can inspect the rock, some of which is glassy obsidian, in the outcrop adjacent to the parking lot. Just down the road, the rhyolite becomes highly brecciated. Its localized thickness, vertical flow-banding, and breccia suggest the rhyolite vented from the area around the dam site.

42 LAKE OWYHEE STATE PARK
Dikes Bake the Succor Creek Formation

Owyhee Reservoir stretches southward behind Owyhee Dam, filling Owyhee Canyon for 53 miles to an average depth of 81 feet. See site 41 for a discussion of the geology along the road to the dam and the rhyolite in which the dam is anchored. The paved road continues beyond the dam and ends at Indian Creek Campground just over 4 miles away in Lake Owyhee State Park.

A quarter mile beyond the dam the rhyolitic breccia gives way to younger lahars of the Succor Creek Formation, distinctive because they actually look like what you'd imagine in a volcanic mudflow: a mix of various-sized rocks suspended in a muddy or sandy matrix. Several basaltic dikes, which likely fed the Owyhee Basalt in the cliffs above, cut the lahars. They display beautiful examples of baked zones, where the original rock was heated by the intruding magma, and chilled margins, where the magma cooled extra quickly against the original rock.

Just past the boat launch, the road climbs, passing many more dikes. The view southward along the shoreline here shows them standing up in relief against the easily eroded Succor Creek Formation. In another quarter mile, a fault drops Owyhee Basalt down to road level, but because of the gentle northward tilt of the rocks you pass back into sandstone of the Succor Creek Formation in less than a half mile.

At the far west end of Indian Creek Campground, you can inspect a flow of Owyhee Basalt with a well-developed breccia along its base that grades upward into some crude columns. The small peninsula in front of the campground is held up by a thick basaltic dike with beautiful columns at the water's edge, formed by cooling of the basalt after it intruded. Some thin patches of Succor Creek Formation stand as narrow fins, made more resistant to erosion from the baking effect of the dike. At the very end of the peninsula, the dike abuts the Succor Creek Formation along a fault.

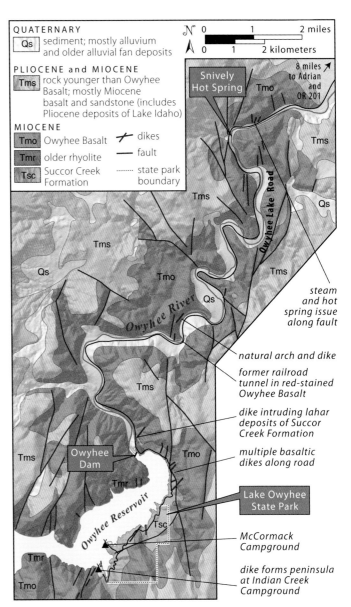

QUATERNARY
Qs sediment; mostly alluvium and older alluvial fan deposits

PLIOCENE and MIOCENE
Tms rock younger than Owyhee Basalt; mostly Miocene basalt and sandstone (includes Pliocene deposits of Lake Idaho)

MIOCENE
Tmo Owyhee Basalt
Tmr older rhyolite
Tsc Succor Creek Formation

✚ dikes
— fault
‥‥‥ state park boundary

Geology of the Owyhee River Canyon and Lake Owyhee State Park.
—Simplified from Ferns and others, 1993a

The basaltic dikes are more resistant to erosion than the Succor Creek Formation, so they stand as fins along the road to the campground.

The view across the lake from Indian Creek Campground shows the same rhyolite that supports Owyhee Dam sitting on top of the Succor Creek Formation instead of below it, as it is at the dam. This relation indicates that deposition of the Succor Creek Formation continued after the rhyolite erupted. You can also see a normal fault that drops the northeast side down, so that Owyhee Basalt comes down to lake level.

A basaltic dike intrudes lahar deposits of the Succor Creek Formation. The orange color in the lahar deposits formed because of the high temperatures in the intruding magma.

Succor Creek Canyon near the south edge of the Succor Creek State Natural Area. All visible rock in the photo is McIntyre Rhyolite.

 43 ## SUCCOR CREEK STATE NATURAL AREA
Thundereggs in Rhyolite Cliffs

Descending into Succor Creek from either its north or south sides, you can't help but notice the steep red cliffs that frame the canyon. Called the McIntyre Rhyolite, the rock erupted 15.9 million years ago, only 100,000 years before the eruption of the nearby Leslie Gulch Tuff (site 44) and at the same time as many of the Columbia River Basalt Group eruptions. The McIntyre lavas flowed over a landscape eroded in the underlying Succor Creek Formation, which is sometimes spelled *Sucker* in the literature. The formation consists of well-bedded, volcanic-rich sandstone, mudstone, and tuffs deposited in lakes and rivers. The landscape probably also hosted wetlands when the rhyolite erupted. Rising gases from the interaction of hot lava over the wet ground created a zone of large air bubbles near the lava's base. Called

lithophysae, these bubbles were later filled by colorful silica-rich material to create thundereggs, Oregon's state rock.

While driving southward down the Succor Creek Road, you can see many good exposures of both the Succor Creek Formation as well as the overlying rhyolite. A good place to collect thundereggs is from the campground, where you can climb a steep grassy slope to the base of the rhyolite cliffs. Continuing southward on the road, you rise through more of the Succor Creek Formation to a low pass. Looking northward, you can see how the rhyolite descends eastward along faults to the level of the creek. Erosion along one of these faults may explain why the valley is so narrow and steep. In another 10 miles south, you reach the turn-off for Leslie Gulch.

Main sources and further reading: Benson and Mahood, 2016; Ferns, 1997; Ferns and others, 1993b; Lawrence, 1988

Hunt for thundereggs along the base of the McIntyre Rhyolite cliffs above the campground.

To reach Succor Creek State Natural Area from the north, turn off OR 201 onto the gravel Succor Creek Road about 20.5 miles south of Nyssa.

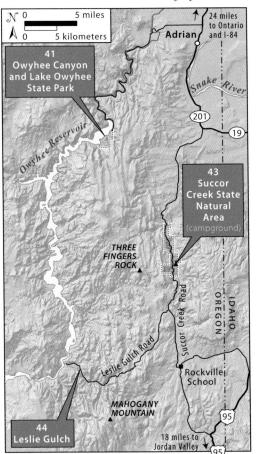

The base of the McIntyre Rhyolite in an exposure along the road contains rounded thundereggs. Inset shows a close-up of their shapes, although the accessible ones are largely broken.

Towers and slopes of Leslie Gulch Tuff on either side of the gravel road.

 **LESLIE GULCH**
Colorful Tuff of the Rooster Comb Caldera

Leslie Gulch presents a wonderland of multicolored spires, cliffs, steep slopes, and canyons. Except for some equally interesting dikes, it's all tuff—rock hardened from ash flows from the cataclysmic eruption of the Rooster Comb caldera 15.8 million years ago. The series of ash flows filled the collapsing caldera. A well-maintained gravel road (see map for previous site) descends Leslie Gulch, which drains steeply into Lake Owyhee.

The Leslie Gulch Tuff forms both slopes and cliffs. After formation of the caldera, hydrothermal fluids altered the tuff and depending on the style of alteration, the rock became unusually resistant or susceptible to erosion. The yellow to

reddish cliffs and spires of Leslie Gulch contain abundant hydrothermal quartz and albite feldspar and are resistant to erosion, whereas the gray to greenish slopes contain abundant zeolite minerals and so are susceptible to erosion. Until recent mapping and geochemical studies showed it was all the same rock, most researchers thought the cliff-formers and slope-formers were two separate tuffs from two separate calderas and named them for Mahogany Mountain to the south and Three Fingers Rock to the northeast.

Many of the cliffs are pockmarked with countless holes and alcoves that resemble honeycombs. Called tafoni, these features form because the outer surfaces of the rock

Main sources and further reading: Benson and Mahood, 2016; Ferns, 1997; Ferns and others, 1993b

The road crosses this rhyolite dike about a third of the way down the canyon. Note its many horizontal fractures.

Honeycomb weathering (tafoni) is prevalent in the cliff-forming unit of the Leslie Gulch Tuff. The dark-reddish crags at the top of the photo are part of a rhyolite dike that intruded the tuff soon after collapse of the caldera.

become hardened through time, as material within the rock dissolves in pore water and reprecipitates on the surface. Simultaneously, the interior of the rock becomes softer. Once the outer crust yields to weathering, the interior of the rock is exposed and weathers out more quickly.

Besides the fantastic scenery, you can't miss the vertical, dark-red rhyolite dikes that cut through the tuff. These dikes likely intruded soon after the caldera collapsed. Many of them show horizontal fractures that look like stacked wood. The fractures form perpendicular to their margins as the magma cools and contracts. The road passes an unusually thick dike about a third of the way to Lake Owyhee as it crosses a cattle guard.

45 COFFEEPOT CRATER OF THE JORDAN CRATERS LAVA FIELD
Eruption of Young Pahoehoe Lava

Out of the way and remote—but definitely worth the long drive—Coffeepot Crater and its lava field is one of Oregon's youngest volcanic features. The 26-mile-long gravel road from US 95 is well-graded except for the last mile. The parking lot ends at the side of Coffeepot Crater and on the edge of the lava field. Be extremely careful if you walk out onto the lava field because many of the unforgiving surfaces are prone to collapse into underlying lava tubes.

Basalt of the Jordan Craters lava field spilled southeastward out of Coffeepot Crater to cover an area of 26 square miles. Some 7 miles to the southeast, it blocked the drainage of Cow Creek to form Upper and Lower Cow Lakes, and about 4 miles to the south, it flowed around a ridge to block some smaller drainages. A piece of charred wood from the deepest sediment in Upper Cow Lake yielded a radiocarbon age of 3,200 years, indicating that the lake, and therefore the lava, can't be any older. In addition to the wonderful curving, ropelike patterns in the pahoehoe lava, the field hosts lava channels; collapse pits, some of which mark lava tubes; and countless tumuli, which bow upward and crack because of pressure from lava flowing underneath.

Coffeepot Crater is about 260 feet deep when measured from the highest point on its rim and contains the remnants of a small lava lake that is now partially covered by eroded debris from the rim. The crater walls consist mostly of cinders and spatter, much of which appears glued together because of the high temperatures. From the rim, you can see that several intact lava flows also form the south wall. The crater likely followed an evolution typical of many cinder cones, with early explosive eruptions that built the cinder cone followed by less-explosive, lava-producing eruptions that created the lava field.

Several small spatter cones, formed by the accumulation of lava fragments that weld together, extend in a line for about 1,000 feet to the west-southwest of Coffeepot Crater suggesting the presence of a subsurface crack. This crack leaked lava from the main cone and produced the small lava field on the southwest side of the cone.

View eastward over Coffeepot Crater and its lava field. Note the partially covered lava lake at its bottom.

Main sources and further reading: Chitwood, 1994; Ferns and others, 1993b; Otto and Hutchison, 1977

Coffeepot Crater, with its small lava field and spatter cones on its southwest side and the larger field to the east in the middle distance. The parking lot is on the right side of the cinder cone.

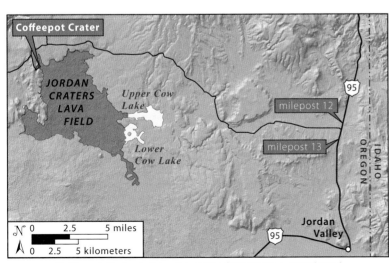

Coffeepot Crater is 26 miles west of US 95 on a gravel road.

Basaltic spatter deposits on the edge of one of the spatter cones.

A pillar of the Rome beds at sunrise.

46 PILLARS OF ROME
Cliffs of Miocene Lakebeds and Stream Deposits

Near Rome, Oregon, the Owyhee River cuts through a broad terrace of alluvial deposits to reveal the underlying Rome beds—light-colored sedimentary rocks of Miocene age. These rocks cover an area of more than 20 square miles and erode to form a series of imposing 60-foot-high cliffs and columns resembling the ancient pillars of Rome, Italy.

If you look closely at the rocks, you'll see that they're mostly mudstone and siltstone with some lenses of volcanic-rich sandstone and conglomerate. The mudstone and siltstone, which in some places contain fossilized fish bones and tiny crustaceans called ostracods, were deposited in a lake. The sandstone and conglomerate likely formed as deposits of a braided stream that flowed into the lake. Some

beds of tuff also lie within the sequence, ash that settled into the lake from erupting volcanoes.

The composition of the cliffs changes if you travel southwest or northeast through the area. To the southwest, the Rome beds contain proportionately more stream deposits, whereas to the northeast they contain more lake deposits to suggest the Pillars of Rome lie near the lake's southwestern shore. As the water level rose and fell, the lake's shoreline migrated back and forth so that deposits of adjoining environments are found side by side as well as on top of each other.

Similar deposits show up northward along the Owyhee River for another 20 miles, indicating the lake extended

 Main sources and further reading: Ferns and others, 1993b; Sheppard, 1987; Wolf and Ellison, 1971; Wood and Clemens, 2002

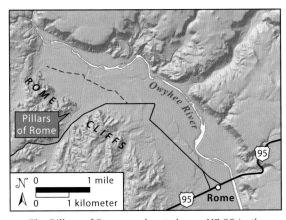

The Pillars of Rome are located near US 95 in the southeastern corner of Oregon.

Pebble conglomerate of the Rome beds were deposited by a stream flowing into a lake.

well beyond the Rome area. Some researchers argue that it was a finger of Lake Idaho, which covered the Snake River Plain from Twin Falls, Idaho, to northwest of Ontario, Oregon. Lake Idaho experienced numerous fluctuations in lake level, existing from as long ago as 9.5 million years to as recently as 4 or 3 million years ago. It drained abruptly when a tributary of the north-flowing Salmon River eroded southward far enough to intersect one of the lake's northern reaches in today's Hells Canyon (site 56).

The Rome beds consist mostly of lakebeds with some river deposits. Near the northeast edge of the cliffs, the river gravels appear as thin greenish beds as shown by the arrow.

111

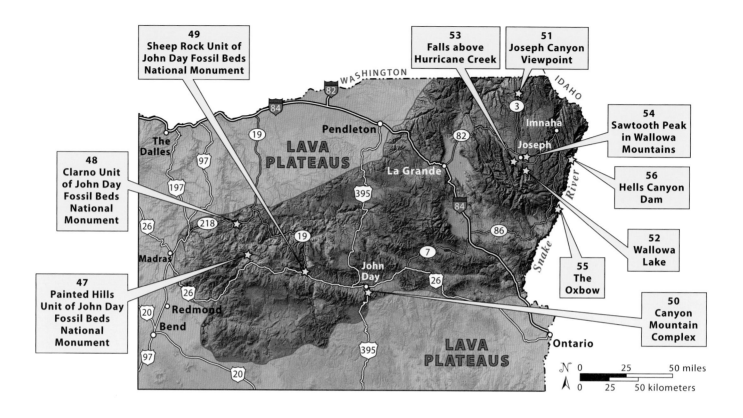

BLUE MOUNTAINS

Geologically and topographically, the Blue Mountains are perhaps Oregon's most variable region. It hosts several accreted terranes and stitching plutons, as well as overlying sedimentary and volcanic rocks. Most of the lavas of the Columbia River Basalt Group, which flowed through five of Oregon's six geologic provinces, originated in, and cover much of, the Blue Mountains. Where erosion removed the basalt, you can see beneath it to more sedimentary and volcanic rock, including deposits of the John Day area. Where erosion removed those rocks, you can see the accreted basement terranes. Beautiful exposures of the Wallowa terrane occur in the Wallowa Mountains and Hells Canyon. It formed as an island arc complex somewhere in the Pacific Ocean. Most recently, glaciers carved U-shaped valleys and left behind glacial moraines, jumbled piles of debris that melted out of the ice.

JOHN DAY FOSSIL BEDS NATIONAL MONUMENT

The John Day Fossil Beds National Monument consists of three separate park units, each 20 to 30 miles apart, that together reflect the geology of some 10,000 square miles of central Oregon. The red, green, and brown rocks create some of Oregon's most colorful landscapes and preserve a world-class trove of mammal and plant fossils. The information from these rocks and fossils paint a detailed picture of changing environments and climate in central Oregon from the Eocene through the Miocene Epochs, between about 50 and 5 million years ago.

From oldest to youngest, the rocks of the John Day area consist of a few small outcrops of accreted terranes, some Cretaceous rock, the Clarno Formation, John Day Formation, Picture Gorge Basalt, Mascall Formation, and the Rattlesnake Formation, which includes the Rattlesnake Ash-Flow Tuff. In general, the Clarno Formation was deposited among stratovolcanoes in tropical to subtropical climates whereas the John Day Formation formed in open floodplains as the climate cooled. The Picture Gorge Basalt, which is part of the Columbia River Basalt Group, and the overlying Mascall Formation formed during a return to wet and warm conditions. The Rattlesnake Formation, deposited at the end of the Miocene Epoch, marks a return to cooler and dryer climates.

Each park unit highlights a different part of the complete record. The Clarno Unit (site 48), some 30 miles west of the town of Fossil, offers extensive exposures of the Clarno Formation, including the spectacular eroded towers of the Palisades. The Painted Hills Unit (site 47), some 10 miles from the town of Mitchell, presents intensely colorful beds near the base of the John Day Formation. The Sheep Rock Unit (site 49), near the town of Dayville, is the largest unit, and presents the upper part of the John Day Formation and younger rocks, as well as the older Goose Rock Conglomerate, deposited in Cretaceous time after accretion of the underlying basement.

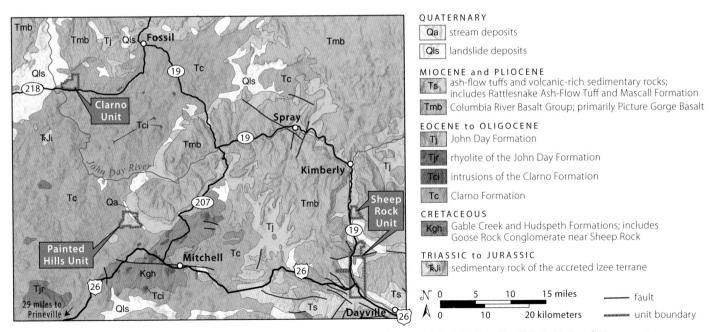

Geologic map showing of the Painted Hills, Clarno, and Sheep Rock units of the John Day Fossil Beds National Monument.

47 PAINTED HILLS UNIT OF JOHN DAY FOSSIL BEDS
Colorful Soils from Tropical Climates

The Painted Hills Unit, arguably the most colorful part of the John Day Fossil Beds National Monument, highlights the lower part of the John Day Formation. Most of these rocks consist of ancient soils developed on volcanic ash-fall deposits, probably from eruptions in the Wildcat and Crooked River calderas (site 33) some 15 and 30 miles to the west, respectively, and the early volcanoes of the Western Cascades. After falling to the ground, the ash gradually turned into soil before being covered by fallout from subsequent eruptions.

In a general way, the colors of these ancient soils reflect the climate in which they formed. The most colorful deposits belong to the Big Basin Member, which forms the base of the John Day Formation. Its deep-red colors mark the most intensively weathered soils, typical of warmer, wetter climates. You can best see these rocks, as well as some red rocks at the top of the underlying Clarno Formation, on the Painted Cove Trail, at the northern tip of the monument. The tan and yellow colors above them suggest less intensive weathering, typical of more temperate climates.

The short trail to Carroll Rim ascends through the lower part of the Turtle Cove Member up to the Picture Gorge Ignimbrite, which caps the rim. (The ignimbrite is a 28.7-million-year-old tuff, more than 10 million years older than the basalt of the same name.) From the rim, you can see the younger deposits, formed during less intensive weathering and generally showing less intensive coloration.

Leaf fossils present in all units suggest a similar climatic shift, with more tropical varieties like banana and palm leaves near the bottom giving way to those of metasequoia and sycamore higher up—and even grasses above those. Microfossils, like pollen and phytoliths—tiny beads of silica that form within plants—also indicate climatic cooling.

The vivid colors of the John Day Formation derive from ancient soils.

Main sources and further reading: Dillhoff and others, 2009; Robinson, 1987

Light-pink dacite (bottom) at the top of the Clarno Formation is overlain by a dark-red soil at the base of the John Day Formation. Viewed along the Painted Cove Trail.

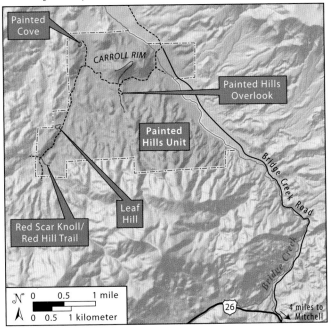

Hiking areas in the Painted Hills Unit of John Day Fossil Beds National Monument.

Carroll Rim is capped by tilted Picture Gorge Ignimbrite that overlies the lower part of the Turtle Cove Member of the John Day Formation. These units slope down to the northeast because of folding.

115

48 CLARNO UNIT OF JOHN DAY FOSSIL BEDS
Palisades of Eroded Mudflows

Some 200 feet high, the rock spires of the Palisades provide drama to an otherwise rolling landscape of the Clarno Unit of John Day Fossil Beds National Monument. Several short hiking trails access the base of the cliffs and allow inspection of the many large, fallen boulders. The Palisades eroded from lahars, mudflows that typically form on volcanoes as avalanches of rock become entrained in slurries of fluidized mud and sand. Each layer of the Palisades marks a separate lahar. The layers are full of broken volcanic rock fragments embedded in a fine-grained matrix. Individual fragments are mostly andesite, suggesting they came from stratovolcanoes. The large size of the fragments suggest the volcanoes were nearby. You can see tree trunks in the cliffs and numerous leaf fragments in many of the fallen rocks, picked up by the lahars as they overran a forest. The plant fossils are tropical species, mostly cycads and palms and tropical varieties of sycamore that grew in a warm and wet climate.

The lahars are part of the Clarno Formation, deposited between 48 and 39 million years ago. The rolling hills around the Palisades consist of other Clarno rocks, including lava flows, tuffs, claystones, and some conglomerate. The rocks contain a host of other fossils and features that also suggest a tropical climate. The plant fossils include palms and bananas, as well as the Clarno nut bed assemblage, possibly the Earth's most diverse collection of fossilized wood. Animal fossils include *Patriofelis*, a catlike predator; *Pristichampsus*, which resembled today's crocodile; and amynodonts, similar to rhinoceros.

The Palisades of the Clarno Formation consist of eroded lahars.

Close-up of a sample from the Clarno nut beds, showing numerous pieces of wood and nuts. This specimen is on display in the Thomas Condon Paleontology Center at the Sheep Rock Unit of John Day Fossil Beds National Monument. View is about 6 inches across.

Hiking area in the Clarno Unit of John Day Fossil Beds National Monument.

Picture Gorge
Ignimbrite

Sheep Rock as seen from near the Thomas Condon Paleontology Center.

 ## SHEEP ROCK UNIT OF JOHN DAY FOSSIL BEDS
Picturesque Rocks along the John Day River

The prominent, pyramid-shaped peak about 1 mile southeast of the Thomas Condon Paleontology Center on OR 19 is Sheep Rock, a sedimentary spire capped by the erosionally resistant Picture Gorge Basalt. Below the basalt are beds of the Turtle Cove Member of the John Day Formation, mostly paleosols formed from ash-fall deposits. Together, they show a gradual lightening of color upward, consistent with a cooling climate and accompanying soil development. Much of the Turtle Cove is green, the result of the green mineral celadonite, which forms through chemical alteration of volcanic ash. The faulted thick brown cliff about halfway up Sheep Rock is the Picture Gorge Ignimbrite, which erupted 28.7 million years ago. Some prominent white ash beds lie beneath it.

You can see the basalt that caps Sheep Rock up close in Picture Gorge, 2 miles south of the paleontology center. The basalt, part of the Columbia River Basalt Group, erupted 16 million years ago from fissures near the town of Monument, about 30 miles to the northeast. Look for beautiful examples of colonnades and entablatures, as well as bright-red paleosols within the canyon. A period of warming during the eruption of the Picture Gorge Basalt continued through deposition of the lower part of the Mascall Formation and is known as the Mid-Miocene thermal optimum. The warm climate then gave way to increasingly cooler and drier conditions as recorded by the middle part of the Mascall through the Rattlesnake Formation.

Site continues on next page ————▶

The Mascall Overlook, off US 26 at the south end of Picture Gorge, provides a sweeping view of the younger rocks of the John Day Basin. The Mascall forms the tan and gray beds above the Picture Gorge Basalt, and the 7-million-year-old Rattlesnake Ash-Flow Tuff, which lies near the bottom of the Rattlesnake Formation, forms the cap of the prominent, tilted surface on the horizon. Like

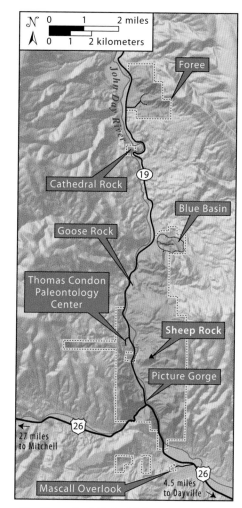

View from the Mascall Overlook. The Mascall Formation forms the tilted, light-colored beds in the foreground. The Rattlesnake Ash-Flow Tuff forms the less-steeply tilted caprock in the background.

The Sheep Rock Unit of John Day Fossil Beds National Monument provides great insights into Oregon's changing environment.

118

the John Day Formation, the Mascall Formation consists of more than 1,000 feet of mostly fine-grained ash that settled out of the air from eruptions in the Western Cascades and possibly even the McDermitt caldera on the Oregon-Nevada border. Later, the ash-fall material was redeposited in lakes and floodplains and transformed into soil. The high clay content of the Mascall, along with infrequent downpours in an otherwise arid climate, contributes to the dramatic badlands erosion, with gullied, vegetation-free slopes.

The Rattlesnake Ash-Flow Tuff formed 7 million years ago by a catastrophic eruption centered near Burns (site 39). Notice how it is tilted less steeply than layers of the underlying Mascall Formation. Their angular discordance marks a time of folding and erosion that occurred between deposition of the two rock units.

Less than 2 miles north of the paleontology center, Cretaceous-age conglomerate shows up on both sides of the road. This older rock, brought to the surface by a normal fault on its north side, was deposited by streams flowing westward over the top of accreted terranes, soon after they became part of North America. If you look closely at the rock, you'll see it contains numerous rhyolitic and some chert cobbles and pebbles, derived from these accreted terranes. You can also see cross-bedded sandstone, which contains fragments of wood in places. The Goose Rock Conglomerate sits directly below the John Day Formation at this locality, without any intervening Clarno Formation. Either the Clarno was never deposited here or was eroded prior to deposition of the John Day.

The John Day River cuts a narrow passage through the erosion-resistant Goose Rock. Inset shows a close-up of the multicolored pebbles and cobbles of the Goose Rock conglomerate.

50 CANYON MOUNTAIN COMPLEX
Earth's Mantle Rock Fed Canyon City Mines

Canyon City, situated along Canyon Creek near the foot of the Strawberry Mountains, was a mining center for eighty years, beginning with the discovery of gold in Canyon Creek in 1862. While prospecting in these mountains, miners found unusual rocks, the value of which became more apparent in the industrial age. Much of the northern front of the Strawberry Mountains consists of peridotite, the rock of Earth's mantle, and serpentinite, formed from low-temperature metamorphism and hydration of peridotite. During World War I, miners worked pod-shaped deposits rich in chromite, which formed within the peridotite and serpentinite.

Just south of Canyon City near milepost 2, US 395 passes bright-green, highly broken outcrops of serpentinite. Up close, you can see why the serpentinite is so broken and shiny—it's made mostly of serpentine minerals, named for their scaly green likenesses to snakes. Antigorite, the main serpentine mineral in these rocks, tends to fill cracks as veins and coat the rock in smooth sheets. Between the veins you can typically see a grayish matrix of magnesium-rich and iron-rich oxides, some of which are even magnetic. During its transformation from peridotite, the serpentinite greatly expanded and cracked. The fractures allowed increased movement of hydrating fluids, which caused even more expansion, cracking, and fluid flow until very little or none of the original rock remained.

The peridotite and serpentinite have been dated at 278 million years. Gabbro, which shows up along the highway as dark-gray cliffs between mileposts 3 and 5, and other igneous rocks as young as 250 million years intrude the mantle rocks and form the top of the range and its southern slopes. Together, the peridotite, serpentinite, gabbro, and other igneous rocks, which include a plagioclase-rich granite, define the Canyon Mountain Complex. Most researchers think the complex formed as a piece of upper mantle overlain by oceanic crust, but its specific origin is still unknown. Whether it was a piece of mid-ocean lithosphere, the roots of an island arc, or part of a smaller ocean basin remains a subject of debate.

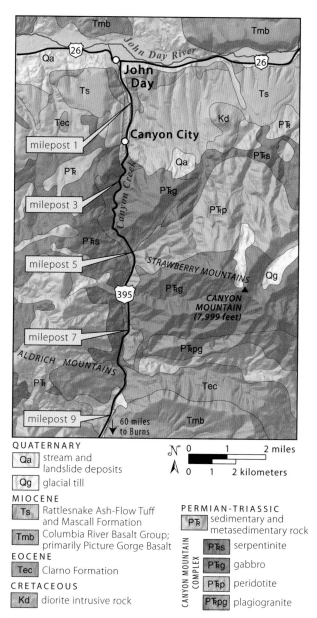

Geologic map of the Canyon Mountain Complex along US 395.

QUATERNARY
Qa stream and landslide deposits
Qg glacial till

MIOCENE
Ts Rattlesnake Ash-Flow Tuff and Mascall Formation
Tmb Columbia River Basalt Group; primarily Picture Gorge Basalt

EOCENE
Tec Clarno Formation

CRETACEOUS
Kd diorite intrusive rock

PERMIAN-TRIASSIC
P℞ sedimentary and metasedimentary rock

CANYON MOUNTAIN COMPLEX
P℞s serpentinite
P℞g gabbro
P℞p peridotite
P℞pg plagiogranite

120   Main sources and further reading: Brown and Thayer, 1966; Mullen, 1983

Outcrop of serpentinite along US 395 near milepost 2.

US 395 winds through the Canyon Mountain Complex just south of Canyon City. This photo, looking north from near milepost 5, shows outcrops of gabbro.

51 JOSEPH CANYON VIEWPOINT
Flows of the Grande Ronde Basalt

Joseph Canyon Viewpoint, about 30 miles north of Enterprise along OR 3, offers an especially accessible and spectacular look at the seemingly uncountable lava flows of the Columbia River Basalt Group. Being 2,000 feet deep at this location, Joseph Canyon exposes about 2,000 feet of lava flows of the Grande Ronde Basalt, a major member of the group. The Grande Ronde lava flows, which erupted from 16.0 to 15.6 million years ago, account for more than 70 percent of the total eruptive volume of the Columbia River Basalt Group. They covered an area of about 65,000 square miles of Oregon, Washington, and western Idaho with a volume of some 36,000 cubic miles. The lavas erupted from the Chief Joseph dike swarm, a series of dikes that cut through older rock across much of northeastern Oregon and southeastern Washington, including Joseph Canyon. With binoculars, one of the dikes is visible on the other side of the canyon. You can see a much thicker dike in the canyon bottom if you stop and look over the rim 3.2 miles north of the viewpoint on the highway.

Continuing northward on OR 3 another 10 miles to the Washington border, you descend 2,000 feet into the canyon of the Grande Ronde River and can inspect many of the flows up close. Just north of the river, in Washington, a large dike forms a free-standing wall on the west side of the highway.

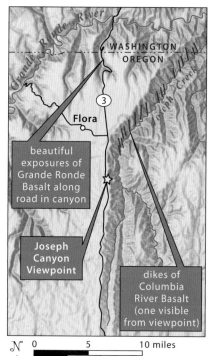

Joseph Canyon Viewpoint, with dikes of the Chief Joseph swarm shown in pink.

View northeastward across Joseph Canyon from the Joseph Canyon Viewpoint. The many lava flows belong to the Grande Ronde Basalt.

Main source and further reading: Reidel and Tolan, 2013; Reidel and others, 2013; Walker, 1979

WALLOWA LAKE
Hemmed in by Glacial Moraines

The easiest way to experience the Wallowa Mountain's glacial history is to drive along the edge of Wallowa Lake south of Joseph. The road is sandwiched between the eastern shore of the lake and a lateral moraine rising steeply to its crest hundreds of feet above. Looking west across the lake, you can see the Wallowa Mountains behind another lateral moraine on the west side of the lake. Northward, the two arms converge into a complex terminal moraine that reaches almost to Joseph. As you look toward the south end of the lake, imagine two lobes of ice, each emerging from an ice cap that covered much of the Wallowa Mountains and pouring down a fork of the Wallowa River to join at the confluence just above the lake. Combined into a single glacier, the ice scoured the valley to a depth of nearly 300 feet. Other lobes spilled down Hurricane Creek, Lostine Creek, and Pine Creek and deposited moraines where they emerged from the mountains.

Studies of the moraine complex at Wallowa Lake find that it records several major advances of ice, the latest one or two advances occurring toward the end of the Pleistocene ice age between about 25,000 to 17,000 years ago. Still older advances, but harder to date and document, occurred some 150,000 years ago and earlier.

A prominent roadcut in the moraine near the north end of the lake shows that it's composed of uncountable boulders, mixed in with cobbles, pebbles, and sand, all derived

Looking south along the eastern glacial moraine and Lake Wallowa to the mountains. Glaciers flowed down the two valleys near the back of the photo and coalesced at the head of today's lake. Note the granitic boulders in the foreground, carried here by ice.

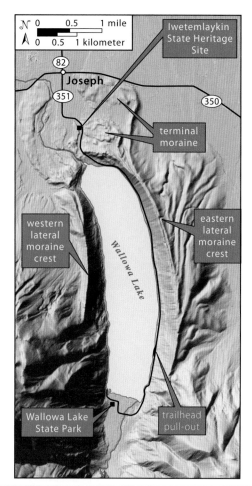

Wallowa Lake is enclosed on its west, north, and east sides by glacial moraines.

from the Wallowa River watershed. Most the rocks are light-colored granitic specimens of the Wallowa batholith, but some consist of Grande Ronde Basalt, while others are rocks of the Wallowa terrane: limestone, thin-bedded sandstone and shale, or greenstone.

You can hike to the eastern lateral moraine's crest from a trailhead halfway between mileposts 4 and 5. The steadily rising trail climbs about 800 feet to spectacular views of the lake, the mountains, and the moraine. An easier, although less dramatic alternative, is to walk the trails at the north end of the terminal moraine at Iwetem-laykin State Heritage Site, its name meaning "at the edge of the lake" in Nez Perce.

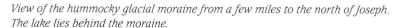

View of the hummocky glacial moraine from a few miles to the north of Joseph. The lake lies behind the moraine.

Roadcut into the eastern lateral moraine showing the assemblage of boulders, cobbles, pebbles, and sand in the glacial till.

View southwest along Wallowa Lake, from the crest of the eastern lateral moraine. Across the lake, you can see the high ridge that forms the western lateral moraine as well as terminal moraine at the end of the lake.

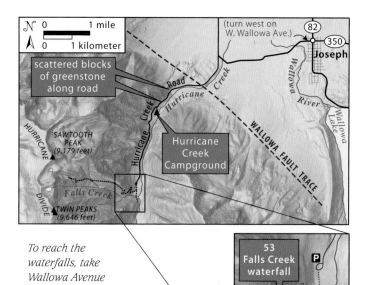

To reach the waterfalls, take Wallowa Avenue west from downtown Joseph, continue past the airport, then watch for a sharp left turn onto Hurricane Creek Road.

53 FALLS ABOVE HURRICANE CREEK
Cascade over Dike-Crossed Wallowa Terrane

In the Wallowa Mountains, the accreted Wallowa terrane is composed of three main rock units: greenstone (metamorphosed basalt), the Martin Bridge Limestone, and the Hurwal Formation. You can inspect the Martin Bridge Limestone and Hurwal Formation in outcrop by taking the short hike to the waterfall on Falls Creek, a tributary to Hurricane Creek. The greenstone, which forms cliffs near the front of the range and on the east side of the valley, appears as fallen blocks along the road to the falls.

Falls Creek originates nearly 3,000 feet above the falls near the summit of Sawtooth Peak (site 54). The waterfall spills over the oldest part of the Hurwal Formation, which consists of fine-grained, deep-ocean turbidite deposits and some limestone. Turbidites form when sand and mud settle to the seafloor from submarine landslides. You can see graded beds in some of the turbidites, where coarse grains lie at the bottom of a sedimentary bed and the grains become progressively finer upward. Three narrow dikes of Columbia River Basalt cut through the rocks at the falls, one of which passes diagonally behind the falling water. If you look closely, you can see a narrow zone of chemical alteration along the dike where the intruding basaltic magma interacted with the sedimentary rocks.

As you approach the falls, you walk beneath a cliff of well-bedded, folded Martin Bridge Limestone. It was deposited in shallower water than the Hurwal and in some places contains fossils that lived only in waters of the far eastern Pacific. Their present residence in eastern Oregon speaks to large-scale tectonic plate motions and continues to spark debate among geologists.

Falls Creek cascades over a diagonal, orange dike that intrudes the Hurwal Formation. Two other dikes, oriented vertically, lie to the right of the falls.

Graded beds in the Hurwal Formation at the falls. The top is to the left, with coarse grains behind the left half of the penny getting finer to the left until just left of the thin, white, calcite-filled fracture, where another coarse bed begins.

 Main sources and further reading: Smith, 1938; Walker, 1979; Weis and others, 1976

54 SAWTOOTH PEAK IN THE WALLOWA MOUNTAINS
The Geologic View from Joseph

The town of Joseph, at the foot of the Wallowa Mountains, offers perhaps the best view of the range's north side, beautifully laying out its geology. The range rises along a normal fault zone to reach elevations higher than 9,000 feet at its serrated peaks, many separated by deep glacial valleys. The straightness of the fault and the abrupt transition from valley floor to mountainside suggest this fault might be recently active.

View of the Sawtooth Peak area, showing the geologic relations between the accreted Hurwal Formation, intrusive granitic rock, and lava flows of the Columbia River Basalt Group.

If you look up the Hurricane Creek drainage to Sawtooth Peak, you can see the following three elements: Below the peak, to its left, lie layered rocks of the Triassic-age Hurwal Formation, part of the accreted Wallowa terrane. Intruding these rocks on their right side is 130-million-year-old granitic rock of the Wallowa batholith. Occupying the top of Sawtooth Peak is the reddish base of the Grande Ronde Basalt, the main phase of the Columbia River Basalt Group.

The Hurwal Formation was deposited in a deep ocean during the Triassic Period as part of an island arc complex. It was later accreted to North America during the latest Jurassic and early Cretaceous Periods. During the accretion, the Hurwal was intruded by the Wallowa batholith. Following the intrusion, which was probably at a depth of about 3.5 miles, everything was uplifted and exposed by erosion to form the land surface over which the Grande Ronde Basalt flowed about 16 million years ago. The basalt now forms an eroded cap on the peak more than 4,000 feet above the same basalt on the valley floor, indicating another period of uplift and erosion *after* its eruption. This recent uplift occurred along the fault at the base of the mountains.

View southward over Joseph to the Wallowa Mountains, uplifted along a normal fault at the front of the range. Hurricane Creek is the deep valley near the center of the photo.

Main sources and further reading: Smith, 1938; Zak, 2012

55 THE OXBOW OF THE SNAKE RIVER
Where Stream Flow Reversed

The Oxbow, where the Snake River takes a hairpin bend upstream from Hells Canyon, didn't form like a typical river meander. Instead, it likely formed when tributaries of the Snake River reversed their flow direction to head northward along what is now the Oregon-Idaho border between 6 to 2 million years ago. Before then, a drainage divide separated northward-flowing tributaries of the Salmon River from tributaries that flowed southward into Lake Idaho. In Miocene time, this large lake covered much of southwestern Idaho and parts of eastern Oregon, fed by the Snake River draining southeastern Idaho. The tributaries of the Salmon River gradually eroded southward into the divide between the two watersheds and captured the flow of some of the south-flowing streams, including Indian Creek and Pine Creek.

According to Tracy Vallier, a longtime geologist of the US Geological Survey, Lake Idaho rose and backed up Indian Creek to the Oxbow during this time. The rising water eroded along several preexisting fault zones to carve a new channel that connected the two captured streams, now flowing northward. The increase in water flowing northward accentuated the erosion, deepened the channel, and further increased the flow until much of Lake Idaho drained, and the Snake River flowed northward down Hells Canyon. The connecting channel, controlled by faults, was highly oblique to the tributaries' overall north-south orientations. This zigzag in the channel eroded into the tight, rounded bends of the Oxbow we see today.

You can see one of the faults as you walk up the gravel road from the gate shown on the map. Looking upriver, follow the contact with your eye between the greenish blocky basement rock and the overlying, well-layered Imnaha Basalt, the oldest part of the Columbia River Basalt Group in northeastern Oregon. Near the river's bend, you can see the contact's position drop on the upstream side of the

The Oxbow on the Snake River is 70 miles east of Baker City via OR 86.

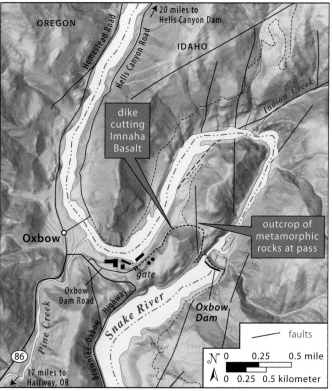

The Snake River didn't flow through here until north-flowing tributaries of the Salmon River breached the drainage divide.

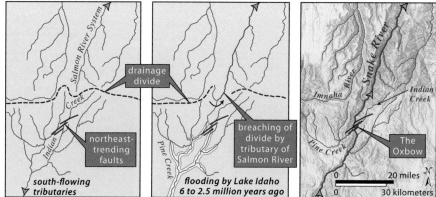

128   Main sources and further reading: Kurz and others, 2016; Vallier, 1998; Wood and Clemens, 2002

View southwestward from the peninsula inside the loop. Pine Creek flows down the canyon in the background to join the river on the right. Oxbow Dam is just out of sight to the left of the photo.

fault. As you continue toward the pass between two high hills, you'll walk below outcrops of the basalt, much of which shows off a beautiful colonnade and some reddish paleosols. Just below the pass, a near-vertical basaltic dike that likely fed younger lavas, cuts through the basalt.

At the pass, look for an outcrop of steeply inclined metamorphic rocks, part of the accreted Wallowa terrane. Because these basement rocks sit higher than the Imnaha Basalt you've just walked through, there must be another fault between them. From the pass, the road turns nearly 180 degrees and descends to the Oxbow Dam, its abutments anchored in the metamorphic rocks.

View northeastward along the Snake River toward one of the faults. The well-layered brown rocks on the left and right side of the photo are Columbia River Basalt Group; in between them is up-faulted basement rock (light-gray rock along the river).

129

HELLS CANYON DAM
Colorful Wallowa Terrane along a Wild River

The Snake River flows freely north of Hells Canyon Dam. From the Hells Canyon Creek Visitor Center, in Oregon just north of the dam, you can follow a trail along this wild river in North America's deepest canyon and inspect the colorful bedrock. You can also explore Hells Canyon Creek, the narrow canyon behind the visitor center. The drive to the visitor center, which follows the Idaho shoreline of Hells Canyon Reservoir above the dam, gives awesome views of the canyon walls on the Oregon side.

The cliffs near Hells Canyon Dam display multiple shades of red, purple, green, and tan, generally colored by iron-bearing minerals. The dark-green rocks owe their colors to the mineral chlorite, which crystallizes during low-temperature metamorphism, whereas the lighter, pistachio greens, typical of many later-formed veins and faults in the rock, comes from the mineral epidote. The shades of red come from varying concentrations of hematite, an iron oxide.

These colorful rocks are part of the Triassic Wild Sheep Creek Formation, mostly basaltic lavas and volcanic breccias with a minor amount of ocean-deposited sedimentary rock. The Wild Sheep Creek Formation is part of the Seven Devils Group that forms most of the outcrops along the river between Oxbow and Hells Canyon dams. The Seven Devils Group is a large fraction of the accreted Wallowa terrane, which originated as an island arc somewhere in the Pacific. At the dam, look also for dark-gray and black basalt among the mix of fallen rocks, some derived from the Wild Sheep Creek Formation, others from the Columbia River Basalt Group that forms the rim of the canyon thousands of feet above.

To reach Hells Canyon Dam, cross the Snake River at Oxbow and drive north for 22.5 miles along the Idaho side of the river and then recross into Oregon on the dam. Set your odometer to find some highlights of the drive. Just north of mile 13, you can see a deposit of 7,700-year-old Mazama Ash next to the road and look across the river to folded Martin Bridge Limestone of the Wallowa terrane underneath Columbia River Basalt Group. Just north of mile 16, you can't miss the colorful exposures of volcanic and sedimentary rocks of the Wild Sheep Creek Formation, and just beyond, spectacular spheroidal weathering in a thick dike of Columbia River Basalt on the east side of the road.

Close-up of different types of alteration of andesite of the Wild Sheep Creek Formation: the red color comes from iron oxide; the dark-green from the mineral chlorite, and the yellow-green from epidote, which came later.

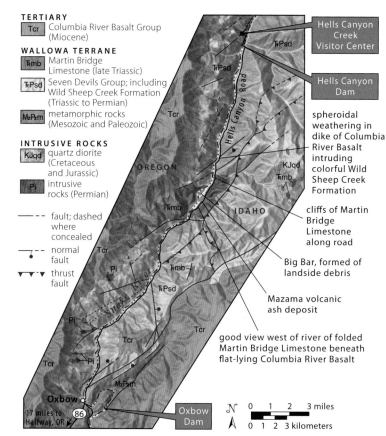

TERTIARY
Tcr — Columbia River Basalt Group (Miocene)

WALLOWA TERRANE
Ťmb — Martin Bridge Limestone (late Triassic)
ŤPsd — Seven Devils Group; including Wild Sheep Creek Formation (Triassic to Permian)
MzPzm — metamorphic rocks (Mesozoic and Paleozoic)

INTRUSIVE ROCKS
KJqd — quartz diorite (Cretaceous and Jurassic)
Pi — intrusive rocks (Permian)

— - - — fault; dashed where concealed

normal fault

thrust fault

Hells Canyon Creek Visitor Center
Hells Canyon Dam
spheroidal weathering in dike of Columbia River Basalt intruding colorful Wild Sheep Creek Formation
cliffs of Martin Bridge Limestone along road
Big Bar, formed of landside debris
Mazama volcanic ash deposit
good view west of river of folded Martin Bridge Limestone beneath flat-lying Columbia River Basalt

Oxbow
17 miles to Halfway, OR
86
Oxbow Dam

0 1 2 3 miles
0 1 2 3 kilometers

Much of the drive to Hells Canyon Dam passes rock of the Wallowa terrane, with flows of the Columbia River Basalt Group on the skyline.

Main source and further reading: Vallier, 1998

Mazama Ash near milepost 13 and folded Martin Bridge Limestone across the river in Oregon.

The Snake River runs free down the deepest canyon in the United States just below Hells Canyon Dam. The bedrock consists of mostly Triassic volcanic rock of the accreted Wallowa terrane.

131

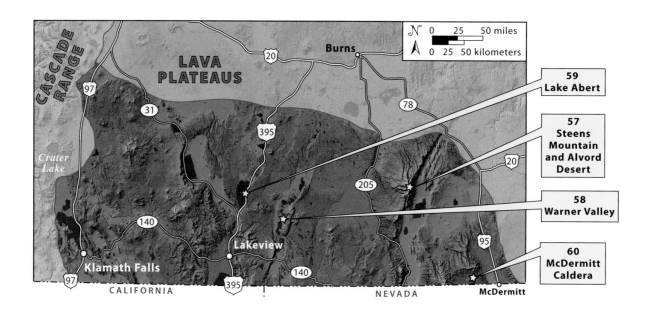

BASIN AND RANGE

The enormous Basin and Range Province extends from the eastern edge of the Sierra Nevada in California east to the Wasatch Front at Salt Lake City, Utah, and from northwestern Mexico north almost to central Oregon. In Oregon, its northern reaches overlap with the Lava Plateaus, and so the boundary between the two provinces can be somewhat arbitrary. As its name suggests, the Basin and Range consists of near-parallel, alternating basins and ranges. Stretching of the Earth's crust produces fault zones along which ranges are uplifted and basins are down-dropped. As a consequence of this faulting, ranges tend to consist of elongate, tilted blocks,

and the basins consist of similarly elongate valleys. One of Oregon's better-known basin and range pairs is the down-dropped Alvord Desert next to the uplifted Steens Mountain.

With the exception of Klamath Lake, the basins in Oregon's Basin and Range don't have river outlets. They tend to fill up with water during rainy times and evaporate during dry times to leave behind deposits of alkali minerals such as halite and gypsum. During the Pleistocene Epoch, when the climate was much wetter, the basins hosted permanent lakes. Their shorelines and deposits are preserved in places along their edges.

Mud-cracked clays of the Alvord Desert with Steens Mountain in the distance.

57 STEENS MOUNTAIN AND ALVORD DESERT
High Alpine Ridge Next to Low Playa

As the crow flies, Steens Mountain and the Alvord Desert are only 5 miles apart, yet they offer completely different experiences. Steens Mountain rises into the alpine world at an elevation of 9,730 feet, is covered by snow much of the year, and supported glaciers during the Pleistocene ice age. The Alvord Desert, more than 1 mile below, is a dry playa with mud cracks left behind after occasional rains. A normal fault separates Steens Mountain on the uplifted side from Alvord Desert on the down-dropped side. As the two sides moved along the fault, they tilted gently westward. As a result, Steens Mountain forms a giant ridge that slopes gently westward but drops precipitously eastward toward the Alvord Desert.

You can drive to the crest of Steens Mountain during summer months along the Steens Mountain Loop, a high clearance route (four-wheel drive recommended) that climbs steadily up the western slope of the mountain to the crest. It follows the crest for about 4 miles and then descends the western slope by a different route. Along the way you gain spectacular views down several U-shaped glacial valleys and have many opportunities to inspect Steens Mountain Basalt overlain, in some places, by the Rattlesnake Ash-Flow Tuff (site 39).

The Steens Basalt marks the onset of eruptions of the Columbia River Basalt Group 16.7 million years ago. The Steens lavas covered an area of some 18,000 square miles

Main sources and further reading: Evans and Geisler, 2001; Hemphill-Haley, 1987; Pezzopane and Weldon, 1993; Reidel and others, 2013; Snyder and others, 1964 and reached a thickness of about 3,000 feet. You can see dozens of these lava flows in the canyon walls, and from the crest of Steens Mountain, you look over the entire sequence south toward Alvord Desert. From the crest, you can also see several basaltic dikes that provided conduits for the rising lavas. Close-up, many of the rocks contains oversized crystals of plagioclase, a type of feldspar that's typical of basalt.

At the Alvord Desert, it's easy to pull off and walk down to the flats. Similar to Lake Abert (site 59) and other ephemeral lakes of the Great Basin, Alvord Desert was a large lake during the wetter climate of the ice age, but as the climate warmed, it dried to a playa, which floods only occasionally.

Several wave-cut benches and ancient shorelines form subtle features along the edge of the playa and indicate a water depth for the ice-age lake of more than 200 feet. Mark Hemphill-Haley of Humboldt State University found evidence for two periods of high lake stands during the Pleistocene.

Hemphill-Haley also mapped the many faults that constitute the Steens fault zone, some of which show up as steps in the alluvial fans where the faults broke the surface; that these fault scarps have not yet eroded attests to the recency of faulting. Alvord Hot Springs, about 4 miles north of Alvord Point, issues from the Alvord fault, one of the largest fault strands. Geophysical studies in the early 1980s found that the Steens Basalt lies some 3,500 feet beneath the playa. When added to the elevation of Steens Mountain, they indicate more than 9,000 feet of slip on the fault zone.

Map of the Steens-Alvord Desert area.

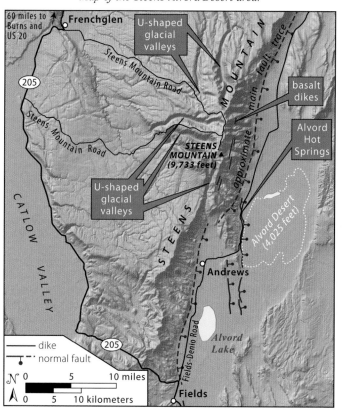

Close-up of the Steens Basalt with large plagioclase crystals.

View to the east up one of the several glacial valleys to the snowcapped summit ridge of Steens Mountain.

View north along the summit ridge of Steens Mountain, showing multiple basalt dikes (steep slanting lines) cutting through the lava flows of the Steens Basalt.

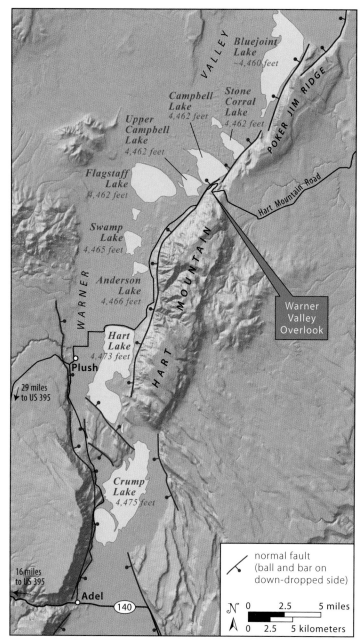

Faults line both sides of the southern half of Warner Valley but only the eastern side of the northern half.

58 WARNER VALLEY
Wet Trough with Flowing Water

Stretching some 40 miles north from the town of Adel, Warner Valley hosts shallow lakes, marshes, and windblown sand deposits set deep in a fault-bounded trough. Like other valleys in Oregon's Basin and Range, its lakes are remnants of a much larger lake that filled the valley between 17,000 and 16,100 years ago. Warner Valley is unusual in that its shallow lakes remain connected, flowing from south to north because the Warner Valley slopes gently northward. Crump Lake, near the south end, maintains a consistent surface elevation of about 4,475 feet; water that rises above this elevation spills northward and flows down the gentle gradient into Hart Lake, only 2 feet lower. From there, it spills northward progressively into each of the lakes. In this way, the lakes maintain a steady inflow and outflow and don't become highly alkaline, like Lake Abert or the Alvord Desert. Only Bluejoint Lake, the final lake at the north end of the valley, has no outlet and frequently precipitates alkali minerals through evaporation. During unusually dry times, water levels fall, and the lakes in the north part of the valley become isolated and, in some cases, completely dry. During unusually wet times, the valley floor becomes covered by myriad small stream channels.

The shape of Warner Valley stems from the faults along its edges that uplifted the adjacent ranges. Faults bound both sides of the southern part of the valley, near Adel, to create a graben, or down-dropped fault block, between uplifted ranges. North of Hart Lake, however, the fault on the western side of the valley appears to die out, while the fault on the eastern side appears to increase in size, uplifting the whole of Hart Mountain in the process. The northern valley forms a half graben, with an abrupt and steep eastern edge and a gradual, gentle western edge. From May to June 1968, the eastern fault system created an earthquake swarm centered on the region between Hart and Crump Lakes, with a maximum magnitude of 5.1.

Main sources and further reading: Pezzopane and Weldon, 1993; Snyder and others, 1964

View northward along Poker Jim Ridge as seen from the Warner Valley overlook on Hart Mountain Road.

View southward along the shoreline of Hart Lake to Hart Mountain (at left), uplifted along a fault and capped by basaltic lava flows. In the distant background at right you can see a ridge uplifted by a fault on the other side of the valley.

Looking south along the edge of precipitated salts of Lake Abert. Abert Rim, on the east side, is a block of Steens Basalt that rises more than 1,000 feet above the lake.

59 LAKE ABERT
Remains of Pleistocene Lake Chewaucan

Lake Abert has no outlet. It's fed by the Chewaucan River, which rises in the mountains west of the town of Paisley. Lake Abert loses its water through evaporation, and a band of white, alkali minerals precipitated by the evaporating water marks the shoreline. During rainy seasons, the lake water rises and reclaims some dry land, redissolving some of the minerals in the process and narrowing the band of alkali. During the hot, dry summer months, however, the lake shrinks again and the band widens considerably.

Lake Abert occupies a basin that typifies southern Oregon's Basin and Range Province. The basin lies on the down-dropped side of a normal fault that runs along the lake's eastern edge, while Abert Rim, rising more than 1,000 feet above the lake, marks the up-thrown side. The rim is Steens Basalt, the oldest major part of the Columbia River Basalt Group. It erupted 16.7 million years ago near what is now Steens Mountain. You can inspect the basalt, distinctive because of its unusually large plagioclase crystals, in the boulders that litter the slopes along the shoreline.

Near the south end of the modern lake, you can see lakebed deposits along the highway, perched about 50 feet above the lake. The lake that existed in the basin during the wetter climates of the Pleistocene Epoch, between about 2.5 million and 10,000 years ago, was enormous. The water body, known as Lake Chewaucan, attained a maximum size of about 460 square miles. On hillsides on both sides of Lake Abert, you can see horizontal lines marking former shorelines of the Pleistocene lake. The highest shorelines indicate the lake was once about 300 feet deep, which easily covered the low divide between Lake Abert and Chewaucan Marsh, as well as the divide between there and the mostly dry Summer Lake! Chewaucan Marsh and Summer Lake display shorelines of this former lake as well.

Main source and further reading: Snyder and others, 1964

Lake Abert and Summer Lake are remnants of Pleistocene Lake Chewaucan.

Deposits of Glacial Lake Chewaucan, some 50 feet above present lake level, as seen along OR 31 halfway between mileposts 85 and 86.

Bird tracks and salt-encrusted rocks along the edge of Lake Abert. View southward with Abert Rim on the right.

139

60 MCDERMITT CALDERA
On the Track of the Yellowstone Hot Spot

Straddling the Oregon-Nevada border, the McDermitt caldera erupted catastrophically 16.35 million years ago, forming the first major caldera in a series that leads across southern Idaho to Yellowstone National Park. It marks part of the Yellowstone hot spot, in which supervolcanoes formed over a localized heat source below the continental lithosphere. As the North American Plate drifted southwestward over the hot spot, it left a trail of major volcanic eruptions that get younger to the northeast.

The McDermitt caldera is huge, measuring some 18 miles long and 25 miles wide. Its major eruption produced as much as 240 cubic miles of McDermitt Tuff, its main by-product, most of which resides inside the caldera. Some windblown ash from the eruption likely contributed to the Mascall Formation in the John Day area. Unlike most other calderas of this size and age, however, you can actually sense that you're in a caldera when you're inside. A series of ring fractures separates a rim of mostly older rock from the McDermitt Tuff in the caldera's interior. Also within the caldera are younger rhyolitic lavas and intrusions and tuff-rich sedimentary rocks that accumulated in a shallow lake.

Hydrothermal activity continued for more than 1 million years after the caldera collapsed, depositing uranium, gold, mercury, and zirconium along the ring fractures. Between 1933 to 1989, four mines in the caldera collectively produced the most mercury in the United States. In addition, the caldera contains significant deposits of lithium within clays of the tuff-rich sedimentary rocks.

It's an easy drive on decent roads into the caldera from the small town of McDermitt, Nevada, on the Oregon state line. Drive west 4.3 miles on the paved Cordero Road to the Disaster Peak Road and head northwest on well-graded gravel for about another 4 miles to the edge of the caldera. From there, you can continue on the main gravel road or follow a variety of smaller but rougher roads to explore the area.

These light-colored, tuff-rich lakebeds were deposited in the shallow lake that occupied the caldera bottom. The canyon in the background is eroded into the rhyolitic tuff.

Main sources and further reading: Henry and others, 2016 and 2017

View westward toward Disaster Peak (lone peak on the far left) and the northwestern rim of the McDermitt caldera. The light-colored outcrops in front of the rim are deposits from the lake that filled part of the caldera.

Rhyolitic tuff in the interior of the caldera displays flow-banding—layering that resulted from flow of the tuff while it was hot. The cliffs in the background are the northern caldera rim.

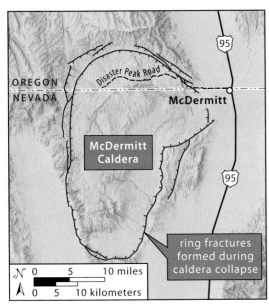

Disaster Peak Road leads into McDermitt caldera. The ring fractures formed during caldera collapse, with down-dropped sides indicated by the hachure lines. —Ring fractures from Henry and others, 2017

GLOSSARY

aa. A common type of basalt flow in which the lava is broken into angular, even sharp-edged fragments.

accreted. Something that has been added onto, such as an accreted terrane added to a continent through plate motions.

alluvial fan. A gently sloping, fan-shaped accumulation of sediments deposited by a stream where it flows out of a narrow valley onto a wider, flatter area.

alluvium. Water-transported sedimentary material.

andesite. A medium- to dark-colored volcanic rock that is between basalt and rhyolite in silica content.

anticline. A fold with the oldest rock in the core; most anticlines have limbs that dip away from the core.

ash. Tiny particles of volcanic glass blown into the air during volcanic eruptions.

ash-flow tuff. The rock formed from the consolidation and compaction of an ash-flow deposit.

asthenosphere. The zone of somewhat malleable rock beneath the lithosphere and over which the lithospheric plates move.

basalt. A dark-colored volcanic rock that contains less than 52 percent silica.

basement. The deepest crustal rocks of a given area. They are typically igneous or metamorphic rock, but some accreted terranes of Oregon are sedimentary in places.

bedding. The layering as seen in a sedimentary rock. A single layer is called a *bed*. When different rock types are interlayered with each other, they are described as *interbedded*.

bedrock. Rock that remains in its place of origin and has not been moved by erosional processes.

blueschist. A metamorphic rock with the blue minerals glaucophane and lawsonite, which form from basaltic rocks under high pressure–low temperature conditions in subduction zones.

breccia. A rock consisting of angular fragments.

caldera. A steep-walled, subcircular depression in a volcano, at least 1 mile across, that formed by collapsing into an emptied or partially emptied magma chamber below.

carbonate. A class of sedimentary rocks, such as limestone or dolomite, that are formed by the combination of atoms of calcium or magnesium with carbon and oxygen.

chert. An extremely fine-grained sedimentary rock made of silica.

cinder. A volcanic rock, typically of basaltic composition, that contains enough air bubbles as to be noticeably less dense than one without air bubbles.

cinder cone. A steep-sided, cone-shaped accumulation of cinders that surrounds a basaltic vent.

cirque. A bowl-shaped basin on a mountain, usually where the head of a glacier once existed.

clast. A grain or fragment of a rock. Clastic rock is sedimentary rock composed of broken fragments, such as sand grains, derived from preexisting rocks.

clay. A sedimentary particle with a grain size less than 0.004 millimeter in diameter.

coal. An organic-rich, dark-colored to black rock that burns. Coal forms from the compaction and long-term, low-temperature heating of plant material.

coarse grained. A term used to describe a rock with large particles or crystals about 1 millimeter in diameter or larger.

colonnade. The part of a basaltic lava flow that shows near-parallel, typically steep fractures that break the rock into columns.

columnar jointing. The fracturing in a lava flow that causes the flow to break into columns.

concretion. A subspherical to irregularly shaped body of well-cemented sedimentary rock that is more resistant to weathering than the rest of the rock.

conglomerate. A sedimentary rock composed of particles that exceed 2 millimeters in diameter.

cross bedding. A layering in sedimentary rock that forms at an angle to horizontal.

crust. The uppermost layer of Earth. Continental crust consists mainly of an igneous and/or metamorphic basement overlain by sedimentary and volcanic rock. Oceanic crust consists of basalt and gabbro.

dacite. A volcanic rock that is intermediate in silica content between andesite and rhyolite.

delta. A nearly flat accumulation of clay, sand, and gravel deposited in a lake or ocean at the mouth of a river.

dike. An intrusive body that cuts across layering in the host rock.

diorite. An intrusive igneous rock that is between gabbro and granite in silica content. It is the intrusive equivalent of andesite.

entablature. The part of a basaltic lava flow that shows numerous closely spaced, typically steep fractures that break the rock into thin, irregular columns.

erosion. The movement or transport of weathered material by water, ice, wind, or gravity.

fault. A fracture or zone of fractures in Earth's crust along which blocks of rock on either side have shifted.

fault scarp. An abrupt cliff or steep section in an otherwise continuous landscape caused by offset along a fault.

feeder dike. A dike of igneous rock that once fed a lava flow.

feldspar. The most abundant rock-forming mineral group. Makes up 60 percent of Earth's crust and contains calcium, sodium, or potassium with aluminum silicate.

fine grained. A term used to describe a rock with small particles or crystals less than about 1 millimeter in diameter.

fissure. An open crack.

floodplain. The portion of a river valley that is built of sediments deposited when the river overflows its banks during flooding.

formation. A body of sedimentary, igneous, or metamorphic rock that can be recognized over a large area. It is the basic stratigraphic unit in geologic mapping. A formation may be part of a larger group and may be broken into members.

fossils. The remains, imprints, or traces of plants or animals preserved in rock.

gabbro. A dark-colored intrusive igneous rock that is less than 52 percent silica. When magma of the same composition erupts at the surface, it forms basalt.

glacial. A term pertaining to a glacier.

glacial till. An unsorted mixture of silt, sand, and gravel left by a melting glacier.

glacier. A large and long-lasting mass of ice on land that flows downhill in response to gravity.

graben. A crustal block that is down-dropped between two inwardly dipping normal faults.

graded beds. Sedimentary layers in which the grain size is coarsest at the bottom and becomes finer toward the top.

granite. A light-colored, coarse-grained igneous rock with a silica content that exceeds 66 percent. It is the intrusive equivalent of rhyolite. The term **granitic** pertains to an igneous rock that resembles and approximates the chemical composition of a granite.

greenstone. Volcanic rocks, typically basalt, that were metamorphosed and developed green metamorphic minerals, such as chlorite and epidote, as a result.

groundwater. The subsurface water contained in fractures and pores of rock and soil.

group. Two or more formations that occur together.

igneous rock. A rock that solidified from the cooling of molten magma or lava.

intrusive igneous rocks. Rocks that cool from magma beneath the surface of Earth. The body of rock is called an **intrusion**.

island arc. An offshore volcanic arc or linear chain of volcanoes formed along a convergent plate margin.

lahar. A volcanic mudflow deposit.

lava. Molten rock erupted on the surface of Earth.

limb. The flank on either side of a fold.

limestone. A sedimentary rock composed of calcium carbonate precipitated in warm water, aided by biological activity.

lithosphere. The outer rigid shell of Earth that is broken into tectonic plates. On average, continental lithosphere is about 100 miles thick and old oceanic lithosphere is about 60 miles thick.

magma. Molten rock within Earth.

mantle. The part of Earth between the core and the outer crust.

marble. Metamorphosed limestone.

marine. Pertaining to the sea.

mélange. A mixture of rocks that may not have formed together. Mélanges can form at a variety of scales and most frequently indicate subduction zone settings.

metamorphic rock. A rock derived from preexisting rock that has changed mineralogically or texturally, or both, in response to changes in temperature and/or pressure, usually deep in Earth.

metamorphism. The recrystallization of an existing rock. Metamorphism typically occurs at high temperatures and often high pressures.

moraine. A mound or ridge of an unsorted mixture of silt, sand, and gravel (glacial till) left by a melting glacier.

mudflow. A mixture of water, mud, and assorted particles that flows downhill in response to gravity.

mudstone. A sedimentary rock composed of mud.

normal fault. A fault in which rocks above the fault move down relative to rocks below the fault. Normal faults result in extension.

obsidian. A volcanic glass, typically high in silica and dark gray to black. Impurities may give rise to brown or red colors.

pahoehoe. A common type of basalt flow in which the lava has a smooth or ropy appearance.

paleosol. A fossil soil.

pebble. A rounded rock particle 0.16 to 2.5 inches in diameter.

peridotite. A low-silica igneous rock that makes up Earth's mantle.

pillow basalt. Basalt that takes on a bulbous pillow shape due to the lava's interaction with water, either from erupting underwater or flowing into it.

plagioclase. A feldspar mineral rich in sodium and calcium. One of the most common rock-forming minerals in igneous and metamorphic rocks.

plate tectonics. The theory that Earth's lithosphere is broken into large fragments, or plates, that move slowly over the somewhat malleable asthenosphere, with intense geological activity at plate boundaries.

platform (wave-cut). A flat bedrock surface eroded by waves and typically exposed at low tide.

playa. An ephemeral lake, one that may fill partially with water during wetter months and dry out partially or completely during dry months.

pluton. A body of intrusive igneous rock. A **stitching pluton** intrudes across the boundaries of two or more terranes.

pumice. A pyroclastic rock that consists of volcanic glass with a frothy texture because of an abundance of air holes.

pyroclastic. Volcanic material that becomes broken into small pieces during an explosive eruption.

quartz. A mineral composed entirely of silica; one of the most common rock-forming minerals.

radiometric dating. The calculation of age based on the rate of time it takes for radioactive elements to decay.

rhyolite. A typically light-colored volcanic rock with more than 66 percent silica. It is the volcanic equivalent of granite.

ribbon chert. A hardened sedimentary rock, composed of microcrystalline silica, with relatively thin, ribbon-like layers.

rift zone. A strip-like area characterized by crustal extension and normal faulting.

sand. Weathered mineral grains, most commonly quartz, between 0.06 and 2 millimeters in diameter.

sandstone. A sedimentary rock made primarily of sand.

sea stack. A tall outcropping of bedrock on a beach or offshore, left as a remnant of an eroding coastline.

sedimentary rock. A rock formed from the compaction and cementation of sediment.

serpentinite. A rock made of minerals of the serpentine group that formed by low-grade metamorphism of iron- and magnesium-rich rocks, usually of the oceanic lithosphere.

shale. A thinly layered rock made of sedimentary particles less than 0.004 millimeter in diameter.

shear. The action caused by the side-by-side sliding of two particles past each other.

shield volcano. A gently sloped volcano typically made of basalt. In profile, shield volcanoes resemble shields.

silica. The compound silicon dioxide. The most common mineral made entirely of silica is quartz.

sill. An igneous intrusion that parallels the planar structure or bedding of the host rock.

silt. Sedimentary particles larger than clay but smaller than sand (between 0.004 and 0.06 millimeter in diameter).

siltstone. A sedimentary rock made primarily of silt.

spit. A long, narrow, fingerlike ridge of sand extending into the water from the shore.

stratovolcano. A steep-sided volcano, typically made of andesite.

strike-slip fault. A fault showing sideways movement or offset of the adjacent rock.

subduction zone. A long, narrow zone where an oceanic plate descends beneath another plate at a convergent boundary.

tectonics. The study of regional-scale deformation of Earth's crust.

tephra. A general term for the material ejected from a volcano.

terrace. An erosional remnant of a former floodplain or coastline standing above the present river or coast.

terrane. A fault-bounded crustal fragment with a geologic history that differs from adjacent fragments.

till. An unlayered and unsorted mixture of clay, silt, sand, gravel, and boulders deposited directly by a glacier.

tuff. A volcanic rock made mostly of consolidated pyroclastic material, chiefly ash and pumice, derived from ash falls or pyroclastic flows. A **welded tuff** is distinctly harder because heat of its particles caused them to weld together.

turbidite. Sands and muds that settle on the seafloor from clouds of sandy, muddy water that flow as submarine density currents. They form alternating layers of sandstone and shale.

vein. A deposit of minerals that fills a fracture in rock.

vent. The actual place where volcanic materials erupt. Vents are either eruptive localities on large volcanoes or mark much smaller volcanoes.

volcanic arc. A chain of volcanoes that forms above an ocean-floor subduction zone.

weathering. The physical disintegration and chemical decomposition of rock at Earth's surface.

zeolite. Aluminum-silicate minerals, containing sodium, potassium, or calcium, that commonly form where volcanic rocks or ash interact with groundwater or volcanic fluids.

REFERENCES

NONTECHNICAL READING

Allen, J. E., Burns, M., and Burns, S. 2009. *Cataclysms on the Columbia*, 2nd ed. Portland: Ooligan Press. Site 31.

Benedict, E. M. 1985. *Diamond Craters Oregon's Geologic Gem*. Bureau of Land Management. Site 40.

Bishop, E. M., and Allen, J. E. 2004. *Hiking Oregon's Geology*, 2nd ed. Seattle: Mountaineers Books. Many sites, general.

Bishop, E. M. 2006. *In Search of Ancient Oregon: A Geological and Natural History*. Portland: Timber Press. General, pertains to most sites.

Bishop, E. M. 2014. *Living with Thunder: Exploring the Geologic Past, Present, and Future of Pacific Northwest Landscapes*. Corvallis: Oregon State University Press. Many sites, general.

Evans, J. G., and Geisler, T. M. 2001. *Geologic Field-Trip Guide to Steens Mountain Loop Road, Harney County, Oregon*. USGS Bulletin 2183. Site 59.

Johnson, L. 2014. *Rockhounding Oregon*. Helena, MT: Falcon Guides. Several sites, general.

Miller, M. B. 2014. *Roadside Geology of Oregon*, 2nd ed. Missoula, MT: Mountain Press. Many sites, general.

Orr, W. N., and Orr, E. L. 2002. *Geology of the Pacific Northwest, 2nd ed*. Long Grove, IL: Waveland Press. Many sites, general.

Vallier, T. 1998. *Islands and Rapids: A Geologic Story of Hells Canyon*. Lewiston, ID: Confluence Press. Sites 55, 56.

OREGON STATE GEOLOGIC MAP AND USEFUL WEBSITES

ACME Laboratories, ACME Mapper 3, acme.com/mapper3/. Excellent source of topographic maps.

Oregon Department of Geology and Mineral Industries (DOGAMI). Dogami.org. Their website offers an interactive map with links to papers and more detailed maps, LiDAR coverage, and links to their publications.

Walker, G. W., and Macleod, N. S. 1991. *Geologic Map of Oregon*. USGS. 1:500,000.

TECHNICAL SOURCES AND FURTHER READING

Anderson, J. L. 1980. Pomona Member of the Columbia River Basalt Group: an intracanyon flow in the Columbia River Gorge, Oregon. *Oregon Geology* 42: 195–199. Site 21.

Armentrout, J. M. 1980. Field trip road log for the Cenozoic stratigraphy of Coos Bay and Cape Blanco, southwestern Oregon. In *Geologic field trips in western Oregon and southwestern Washington*, Oregon Department of Geology and Mineral Resources Bulletin 101, eds. K.F. Oles, J.G. Johnson, A.R. Niem, and W.A. Niem, p. 177–216. Sites 13, 14.

Bacon, C. R. 2008. *Geologic Map of Mount Mazama and Crater Lake Caldera, Oregon*. USGS Scientific Investigations Map I-2832, 4 sheets, scale 1:24,000. Site 28.

Bacon, C. R., and Wright, H. 2017. *Geologic Field-Trip guide to Mount Mazama and Crater Lake Caldera, Oregon*. USGS Scientific Investigations Report 2017–5022–J2. Site 28.

Baldwin, E. M. 1955. *Geology of the Marys Peak and Alsea Quadrangles, Oregon*. USGS Oil and Gas Investigations Map OM 162. Site 10.

Baldwin, E. M. 1956. *Geologic Map of the Lower Siuslaw River Area, Oregon*. USGS Oil and Gas Investigations Map OM 186, 1:62,500. Site 11.

Baldwin, E. M. and Beaulieu, J. D. 1973. *Geology and Mineral Resources of Coos County, Oregon*. Oregon Department of Geology and Mineral Resources Bulletin 80. Sites 13, 15.

Beeson, M. H., and Tolan, T. L. 1987. Columbia River Gorge: the geologic evolution of the Columbia River in northwestern Oregon and southwestern Washington. In *GSA Centennial Field Guide, Cordilleran Section,* ed. M. Hill, GSA, p. 321–326. Site 20.

Beeson, M. H., Perttu, R., and Perttu, J. 1979. The Origin of the Miocene basalts of coastal Oregon and Washington: An alternative hypothesis. *Oregon Geology* 41 (10): 159–165. Sites 1, 2, 3, 4, 5, 7, 8.

Benson, T. R., and Mahood, G. A. 2016. Geology of the Mid-Miocene Rooster Comb Caldera and Lake Owyhee Volcanic Field, eastern Oregon: Silicic volcanism associated with Grande Ronde flood basalt. *Journal of Volcanology and Geothermal Research* 309: 96–117. Sites 43, 44.

Berri, D. A. 1982. *Geology and Hydrothermal Alteration, Glass Buttes, Southeast Oregon*. MS thesis, Portland State University. Site 38.

Bishop, E. M., and Smith, G. A. 1990. A field guide to the geology of Cove Palisades State Park and the Deschutes Basin in central Oregon. *Oregon Geology* 52 (1): 3–12. Site 32.

Bishop, E. M. 1990. Field trip guide to Cove Palisades State Park and the Deschutes Basin. *Oregon Geology* 52 (1): 13–16. Site 32.

Boschman, D. E. 2012. *Structural and Volcanic Evolution of the Glass Buttes Area, High Lava Plains, Oregon*. MS thesis, Oregon State University. Site 38.

Brand, B. D., and Heiken, G. 2009. Tuff cones, tuff rings, and maars of the Fort Rock-Christmas Valley basin, Oregon: Exploring the vast array of pyroclastic features that record violent hydrovolcanism at Fort Rock and the Table Rock Complex. In *Volcanoes to Vineyards: Geologic Field Trips through the Dynamic Landscape of the Pacific Northwest*, GSA Field Guide 15, eds. J. E. O'Connor, R. J. Dorsey, and I. P. Madin, p. 521–538. Site 36.

Brown, C. E., and Thayer, T. P. 1966. *Geologic Map of the Canyon City Quadrangle, Northeastern Oregon*. USGS Miscellaneous Geologic Investigations Map I-447. Site 50.

Cameron, K. A., and Pringle, P. 1986. Post-glacial lahars of the Sandy River Basin, Mount Hood, Oregon. *Northwest Science* 60 (4): 225–237. Site 22.

Camp, V. E., and Wells, R. E. 2021. The case for a long-lived and robust Yellowstone Hot Spot. *GSA Today* 31: 4–10.

Cashman, K. V., Deligne, N. I., Gannett, M. W., and others. 2009. Fire and Water: Volcanology, geomorphology, and hydrogeology of the Cascade Range, central Oregon. In *Volcanoes to Vineyards: Geologic Field Trips through the Dynamic Landscape of the Pacific Northwest*, GSA Field Guide 15, eds. J. E. O'Connor, R. J. Dorsey, and I. P. Madin, p. 539–582. Sites 25, 26, 32, 34.

Chitwood, L. A., Jensen, R. A., and Groh, E. A. 1977. The age of Lava Butte. *The Ore Bin* 39: 157–154. Site 34.

Chitwood, L. A. 1994. Inflated basaltic lava --examples of processes and landforms from central and southeast Oregon. *Oregon Geology* 56: 11–20. Sites 40, 45.

Clemens, K. E, and Komar, P. D. 1988. Oregon beach-sand compositions produced by mixing of sediments from multiple sources under a transgressing sea. *Journal of Sedimentary Petrology* 56: 15–22. Sites 4, 12.

Colón, D. P., Bindeman, I., Wotzlaw, J., Christiansen, E. H., and Stern, R. A. 2018. Origins and evolution of rhyolitic magmas in the central Snake River Plain: Insights from coupled high-precision geochronology, oxygen isotope, and hafnium isotope analyses of zircon. *Contributions to Mineralogy and Petrology* 173 (2).

Cooper, D. M. 1980. Sedimentation, stratigraphy and facies variation of the lower to middle Miocene Astoria Formation in Oregon. PhD dissertation, Oregon State University. Sites 2, 7.

Cooper, W. S. 1958. *Coast Dunes of Oregon and Washington*. GSA Memoir 72. Sites 4, 12.

Covington, S. 2004. *Oregon Caves National Monument Geologic Resources Management Issues Scoping Summary*. National Park Service Geologic Resources Division. Site 18.

Cressy, F. B., Jr. 1973. Stratigraphy and sedimentation of the Neahkahnie Mountain-Angora Peak area, Tillamook and Clatsop Counties, Oregon. MS thesis, Oregon State University. Site 1.

Davis, L. G. 2006. Geoarcheological insights from Indian Sands, a Late Pleistocene site on the southern Northwest Coast, USA. *Geoarcheology* 21: 351–361. Site 16.

Dillhoff, R. M., Dillhoff, T. A., Dunn, R. E., Myers, J. A., and Stromberg, C. A. E. 2009. Cenozoic paleobotany of the John Day Basin, central Oregon. In *Volcanoes to Vineyards: Geologic Field Trips through the Dynamic Landscape of the Pacific Northwest*, GSA Field Guide 15, eds. J. E. O'Connor, R. J. Dorsey, and I. P. Madin, p. 135–164. Sites 47, 48, 49.

Deligne, N. I., Mckay, D., Conrey, R. M., and others. 2017. *Field-trip Guide to Mafic Volcanism of the Cascade Range in Central Oregon: A Volcanic, Tectonic, Hydrologic, and Geomorphic Journey*. USGS Scientific Investigations Report 2017–5022-H. Site 25.

Deligne, N. I., Conrey, R. M., Cashman, K. V., and others. 2016. Holocene volcanism of the upper McKenzie River catchment, central Oregon Cascades, USA. *GSA Bulletin* 128: 1618–1635. Site 25.

Dott, R. H. Jr. 1971. *Geology of the southwestern Oregon coast west of the 124th meridian*. Oregon Department of Geology and Mineral Industries Bulletin 69. Sites 14, 16, 17.

Drew, D. L., Bindeman, I. N., Watts, K.E., and others. 2013. Crustal-scale recycling in caldera complexes and rift zones along the Yellowstone hot spot track: O and Hf isotopic evidence in diverse zircons from voluminous rhyolites of the Picabo volcanic field, Idaho. *Earth and Planetary Science Letters* 381: 63–77.

Evarts, R. C., Conrey, R. M., Fleck, R. J., and Hagstrum, J. T. 2009. The Boring Volcanic Field of the Portland-Vancouver area, Oregon and Washington: Tectonically anomalous forearc volcanism in an urban setting. In *Volcanoes to Vineyards: Geologic Field Trips through the Dynamic Landscape of the Pacific Northwest*, GSA Field Guide 15, eds. J. E. O'Connor, R. J. Dorsey, and I. P. Madin, p. 253–270. Site 19.

Ferns, M. L. 1997. Field trip guide to the eastern margin of the Oregon-Idaho graben and the middle Miocene calderas of the Lake Owyhee volcanic field. *Oregon Geology* 59 (1): 9–20. Sites 43, 44.

Ferns, M. L., Brooks, H. C., Evans, J. G., and Cummings, M. L. 1993a. *Geologic Map of Vale 30 x 60-minute quadrangle, Malheur County, Oregon*. Oregon Department of Geology and Mineral Industries map GMS-77. 1:100,000. Sites 41, 42.

Ferns, M. L., Evans, J. G., and Cummings, M. L. 1993b. *Geologic Map of the Mahogany Mountain 30 x 60-minute quadrangle, Malheur County, Oregon.* Oregon Department of Geology and Mineral Industries map GMS-78. 1:100,000. Sites 43, 44, 45, 46.

Freed, M. 1979. Silver Falls State Park. *Oregon Geology* 41 (1): 3–14. Site 23.

Hart, R. 1997. Episodically buried forests in the Oregon surf zone. *Oregon Geology* 59 (6): 131–143. Sites 6, 13.

Heath, B. A., Hooft, E .E. E., Toomey, D. R., and Bezada, M. J. 2015. Imaging the magmatic system of Newberry Volcano using joint active source and teleseismic tomography. *Geochemistry Geophysics, Geosystems* 16 (12). Site 34.

Hemphill-Haley, M. A. 1987. Quaternary stratigraphy and late Holocene faulting along the base of the eastern escarpment of Steens Mountain, southeastern Oregon. MS thesis, Humboldt State University. Site 57.

Henry, C. D., Castor, S. B., Starkel, W. A., and others. 2016. *Preliminary Geologic Map of the McDermitt Caldera, Humboldt County, Nevada and Harney and Malheur Counties, Oregon.* Nevada Bureau of Mines and Geology, Open-File Report 16-1. Site 60.

Henry, C. D., Castor, S. B., Starkel, W. A., and others. 2017. Geology and evolution of the McDermitt caldera, northern Nevada and southeastern Oregon, western USA. *Geosphere* 13: 1066–1112. Site 60.

Hildreth, W. 2007. *Quaternary Magmatism in the Cascades: Geologic Perspectives.* USGS Professional Paper 1744. Sites 22, 26, 28.

Jensen, R. A., Donnelly-Nolan, J. M., and Mckay, D. 2009. A field guide to Newberry Volcano, Oregon. In *Volcanoes to Vineyards: Geologic Field Trips through the Dynamic Landscape of the Pacific Northwest,* GSA Field Guide 15, eds. J. E. O'Connor, R. J. Dorsey, and I. P. Madin, p. 53–79. Sites 34, 35.

Jensen, R. A., and Donnelly-Nolan, J. M. 2017. *Field-Trip Guide to the Geologic Highlights of Newberry Volcano, Oregon.* USGS Scientific Investigations Report 2017-5022-J2. Sites 34, 35.

Johnson, K. E., and Ciancanelli, E. V. 1984. Geothermal exploration at Glass Buttes, Oregon. *Oregon Geology* 46 (2): 15–20. Site 38.

Jordan, B. T., Streck, M. J., and Grunder, A. L. 2002. Bimodal volcanism and tectonism of the High Lava Plains, Oregon. In *Field Guide to geologic processes in Cascadia, Oregon.* Department of Geology and Mineral Industries Special Paper 36, ed. G. W. Moore, p. 23–46. Site 39.

Kelsey, H. M. 1990. Late Quaternary deformation of marine terraces on the Cascadia subduction zone near Cape Blanco, Oregon. *Tectonics* 9 (5): 983–1014. Site 14.

Kendall, J., Cramer, D., King, R., and Furst, S. 2011. *Geologic Map of Oregon Caves National Monument and Proposed Boundary Expansion.* Oregon Caves National Monument Resources Management Division. Scale 1:8070. Site 18.

Kittleman, L. R. 1973. *Guide to the Geology of the Owyhee Region of Oregon.* Museum of Natural History, University of Oregon Bulletin 21. Sites 41, 42.

Knauss, L. L., Silva, M., and D'Allura, J. 2008. *Pilot Rock: A Late Oligocene Western Cascades Andesite Intrusive, Southern Oregon.* Proceedings of the Oregon Academy of Science 16. Site 29.

Komar, P. D. 1997. *The Pacific Northwest Coast.* Durham, NC.: Duke University Press. Sites 4, 12.

Kurz, G. A., Schmitz, M. D., Northrup, C. J., and Vallier, T. L. 2016. Isotopic compositions of intrusive rocks from the Wallowa and Olds Ferry arc terranes of northeastern Oregon and western Idaho: Implications for Cordilleran evolution, lithospheric structure, and Miocene magmatism. *Lithosphere* 9: 235–264. Site 55.

Lawrence, D. C. 1988. Geologic Field Trip guide to the northern Succor Creek area, Malheur County, Oregon. *Oregon Geology* 50 (2): 15–21. Site 43.

Licciardi, J. M. 2001. Chronology of latest Pleistocene lake-level fluctuations in the pluvial Lake Chewaucan basin, Oregon, USA. *Journal of Quaternary Science* 16 (6): 545–553. Site 52.

Licciardi, J. M., Clark, P. U., Brook, E. J., and others. 2004, Variable responses of western US glaciers during the last deglaciation. *Geology* 32: 81–84. Site 52.

Ma, L., Madin, I. P., Duplantis, S., and Williams, K. J. 2012. *Lidar-Based Surficial Geologic Map and Database of the Greater Portland, Oregon, Area, Clackamas, Columbia, Marion, Multnomah, Washington, and Yamhill Counties, Oregon, and Clark County, Washington.* DOGAMI Open-File Report O-12-02, 1:63,630.

Mackey, B. H., Castonguay, S. R., Wallace, P. J., and Weldon, R. J. 2014. Synchronous late Pleistocene extensional faulting and basaltic volcanism at Four Craters Lava Field, central Oregon, USA. *Geosphere* 10: 1247–1254. Site 37.

MacLeod, N. S., Sherrod, D. R., Chitwood, L. A., and Jensen, R. A. 1995. *Geologic Map of Newberry Volcano, Deschutes, Klamath, and Lake Counties, Oregon.* USGS Miscellaneous Investigations Series Map I-2455. 1:24,000. Sites 34, 35.

Madin, I. P. 2009. Portland, Oregon, geology by tram, train, and foot. *Oregon Geology* 69 (1): 1–20. Site 19.

Mardock, C. L. 1994. A geologic overview of Yaquina Head, Oregon. *Oregon Geology* 56 (2): 27–33. Site 8.

McClaughry, J. D., Ferns, M. L., Gordon, C. L., and Patridge, K. A. 2009A. Field trip guide to the Oligocene Crooked River caldera: Central Oregon's Supervolcano, Crook, Deschutes, and Jefferson Counties, Oregon. *Oregon Geology* 69 (1): 25–44. Site 33.

McClaughry, J. D., Ferns, M. L., Streck, M. J., and others. 2009B. Paleogene calderas of central and eastern Oregon: Eruptive sources of widespread tuffs in the John Day and Clarno Formations. In *Volcanoes to Vineyards: Geologic Field Trips through the Dynamic Landscape of the Pacific Northwest*, GSA Field Guide 15, eds. J. E. O'Connor, R. J. Dorsey, and I. P. Madin, p. 407–434. Site 33.

McClaughry, J. D., Wiley, T. J., Ferns, M. L., and Madin, I. P. 2010. *Digital Geologic Map of the Southern Willamette Valley, Benton, Lane, Linn, Marion, and Polk Counties, Oregon.* Oregon Department of Geology and Mineral Industries Open File Report O-10-03. Site 24.

Mullen, E. D. 1983. Petrology and regional setting of peridotite and gabbro of the Canyon Mountain Complex, northeast Oregon. PhD dissertation, Oregon State University. Site 50.

National Park Service. 2011. *Oregon Caves National Monument Geologic Resources Inventory Report.* National Park Service Natural Resource Report NPS/NRSS?GRD?NRR--2011/457. Site 18.

Niem, A.R. 1975. Geology of Hug Point State Park, northern Oregon coast. *The Ore Bin* 37 (2): 17–36. Site 2.

Otto, B. R., and Hutchison, D. A. 1977. The Geology of Jordan Craters, Malheur County, Oregon. *The Ore Bin* 39 (8): 125–139. Site 45.

Oxford, J. 2006. Early Oligocene intrusions in the central Coast Range of Oregon: Petrography, geochemistry, geochronology, and implications for the Tertiary magmatic evolution of the Cascadia forearc. MS thesis, Oregon State University. Site 10.

Peterson, C. D., Darienzo, M. E., Burns, S. F., and Burris, W. K. 1993. Field trip guide to Cascadia paleoseismic evidence along the northern Oregon coast: Evidence of subduction zone seismicity in the central Cascadia margin. *Oregon Geology* 55: 99–114. Site 6.

Peterson, C. D., Stock, E., Price, D. M., and others. 2007. Ages, distributions, and origins of upland coastal dune sheets in Oregon, USA. *Geomorphology* 91: 80–102. Sites 4, 12, 16.

Peterson, N. V., and Groh, E. A. 1964. Diamond Craters, Oregon. *The Ore Bin* 26: 17–34. Site 40.

Pezzopane, S. K., and Weldon, R. J. II. 1993. Tectonic role of active faulting in central Oregon. *Tectonics* 12: 1140–1169. Sites 37, 57, 58, 59.

Prothero, D. R., and Donohoo, L. L. 2001. Magnetic stratigraphy and tectonic rotation of the middle Eocene Coaledo Formation, southwestern Oregon. *Geophysical Journal International* 145: 223–232. Site 13.

Reidel, S. P., Camp, V. E., Tolan, T. L., Martin, B. S. 2013. The Columbia River flood basalt province: Stratigraphy, areal extent, volume, and physical volcanology. In *The Columbia River Basalt Province*, GSA Special Paper 497, eds. S. P. Reidel, V. E. Camp, M. E. Ross, and others. p. 1–44. Especially relevant to sites 8, 20, 21, 23, 30, 51, 57.

Reidel, S. P., and Tolan, T. L. 2013. The Grande Ronde Basalt, Columbia River Basalt Group, In *The Columbia River Basalt Province*, GSA Special Paper 497, eds. S. P. Reidel, V. E. Camp, M. E. Ross, and others. p. 117–154. Site 51.

Robinson, P. T. 1987. John Day Fossil Beds National Monument, Oregon: Painted Hills unit. In *GSA Centennial Field Guide, Cordilleran Section*, ed. M. Hill, GSA, p. 317–320. Site 47.

Scott, W. E., Gardner, C. A., Sherrod, D. R., and others. 1997. *A Geologic History of Mt. Hood Volcano, Oregon: A Field Trip Guidebook.* USGS Open File Report 97-263. Site 22.

Scott, W. E., and Gardner, C. A. 2017. *Field Trip Guide to Mt. Hood, Oregon, Highlighting Eruptive History and Hazards.* USGS Scientific Investigations Report 2017-5022-G. Site 22.

Seligman, A. N., Bindeman, I. N., McClaughry, J., Stern, R. A., and Fisher, C. 2014. The earliest low and high ^{18}O caldera-forming eruptions of the Yellowstone plume: Implications for the 30-40 ma Oregon calderas and speculations on plume-triggered delaminations. *Frontiers in Earth Science* 2. Site 33.

Sheppard, R. A. 1987. Field trip guide to the Sheaville and Rome zeolite deposits, southeastern, Oregon. *Oregon Geology* 49 (1): 3–10. Site 46.

Sherrod, D. R., Champion, D. E., and McGeehin, J. P. 2012. Age and duration of volcanic activity at Diamond Craters, southeastern Oregon. *Journal of Volcanology and Geothermal Research* 247 and 248: 108–114. Site 40.

Sherrod, D. R. 1991. *Geologic Map of a Part of the Cascade Range between latitudes 43 degrees and 44 degrees, Central Oregon.* USGS Geologic Investigations Series Map I-1291, 1:25,000. Site 27.

Smith, G. 1998. Geology along US Highways 197 and 97 between The Dalles and Sunriver, Oregon. *Oregon Geology* 60 (1): 3–17. Sites 31, 32, 33, 34.

Smith, W. D. 1938. *Geologic Reconnaissance of the Central Portion of the Wallowa Mountains, Oregon.* Oregon Dept of Geology and Mineral Industries Map QM-10. Sites 53, 54.

Snavely, P. D. Jr., and MacLeod, N. S. 1974. Yachats Basalt: An upper Eocene differentiated volcanic sequence in the Oregon Coast Range. *Journal of Research of the USGS* 2: 395–403. Site 9.

Snyder, C. T., Hardman, G., and Zdenek, F. F. 1964. *Pleistocene Lakes in the Great Basin.* USGS Miscellaneous Geologic Investigations Map I-416. Sites 57, 58, 59.

Streck, M., and Ferns, M. 2004. The Rattlesnake Tuff and other Miocene silicic volcanism in eastern Oregon. In *Geological field trips in southern Idaho, eastern Oregon, and northern Nevada,* Rocky Mountain and Cordilleran sections of the GSA annual meeting guidebook, eds. K. M. Haller and S. H. Wood, p. 2–17. Site 39.

Taylor, E. M., and Smith G. A. 1987. Record of High Cascade volcanism at Cove Palisades, Oregon: Deschutes Formation volcanic and sedimentary rocks. In *GSA Centennial Field Guide, Cordilleran Section,* ed. M. Hill, p. 313–315. Site 32.

Taylor, E. M. 1987. Late high Cascade volcanism from summit of McKenzie Pass, Oregon: Pleistocene composite cones on platform of shield volcanoes: Holocene eruptive centers and lava fields. In *GSA Centennial Field Guide, Cordilleran Section,* ed. M. Hill, p. 311–312. Site 26.

Tolan, T. L., and Beeson, M. H. 1984. Intracanyon flows of the Columbia River Basalt Group in the lower Columbia River Gorge and their relationship to the Troutdale Formation. *GSA Bulletin* 95: 463–477. Site 21.

Walker, G. W. 1979. *Reconnaissance Geologic Map of the Oregon Part of the Grangeville Quadrangle, Baker, Union, Umatilla, and Wallowa Counties, Oregon.* US Geological Survey Miscellaneous Investigations Map I-1116. Sites 51, 53.

Weis, P. L., Gualtieri, J. L., Cannon, W. F., and others. 1976. *Geologic and Aeromagnetic Map of the Eagle Cap Wilderness and Proposed Additions, Baker, Union, and Wallowa Counties, Oregon.* USGS Bulletin 1385E, scale 1:62,500. Site 53.

Wells, R. E., Niem, A. R., Evarts, R. C., and Hagstrum, J. T. 2009. The Columbia River Basalt Group: From the gorge to the sea. In *Volcanoes to Vineyards: Geologic Field Trips through the Dynamic Landscape of the Pacific Northwest,* GSA Field Guide 15, eds. J. E. O'Connor, R. J. Dorsey, and I. P. Madin, p. 737–774. Sites 1, 3, 5, 20.

Wells, R. E., Snavely, P. D. Jr., Macleod, N. S., and others. 1994. *Geologic Map of the Tillamook Highlands, Northwest Oregon Coast Range: A Digital Database.* USGS Open-File Report 94-21. Site 4.

Wells, R., Bukry, D., Friedman, R., and others. 2014. Geologic history of Siletzia, a large igneous province in the Oregon and Washington Coast Range: Correlation to the geomagnetic polarity time scale and implications for a long-lived Yellowstone hotspot. *Geosphere* 10: 692–719. Site 10.

Wiley, T. J., McClaughry, J. D., Ma, L., and others. 2014. *Geologic Map of the Southern Oregon Coast between Port Orford and Bandon, Curry, and Coos Counties, Oregon.* Oregon Dept. of Geology and Mineral Industries, Open File Report 0-14-01.

Wolf, K. H., and Ellison, B. 1971. Sedimentary geology of the zeolitic volcanic lacustrine Pliocene Rome Beds, Oregon. *Sedimentary Geology* 6: 271–302. Site 46.J

Wood, S. H., and Clemens, D. M. 2002. Geologic and tectonic history of the western Snake River Plain, Idaho and Oregon. In *Tectonic and Magmatic Evolution of the Snake River Plain Volcanic Province,* Idaho Geological Survey Bulletin 30, eds B. Bonnichsen, C. M White, and M. McCurry, p. 69–103. Sites 46, 55.

Zak, J., Verner, K., Johnson, K., and Schwartz, J. 2012. Magma emplacement process zone preserved in the roof of a large Cordilleran batholith, Wallowa Mountains, northeastern Oregon. *Journal of Volcanology and Geothermal Research* 227: 61–75. Site 54.

INDEX

—MORGAN JUDY PHOTO

Marli Miller is a senior instructor and researcher at the University of Oregon. She completed her BA in geology at Colorado College in 1982 and her MS and PhD in structural geology at the University of Washington in 1987 and 1992, respectively. Marli teaches a variety of courses, including introductory geology, structural geology, field geology, and geophotography. In addition to numerous technical papers, she is the author of *Roadside Geology of Oregon*, *Roadside Geology of Washington* with coauthor Darrel Cowan, and *Geology of Death Valley National Park* with coauthor Lauren A. Wright. Marli has two daughters, Lindsay and Megan.